Robert Goddard
Space Pioneer

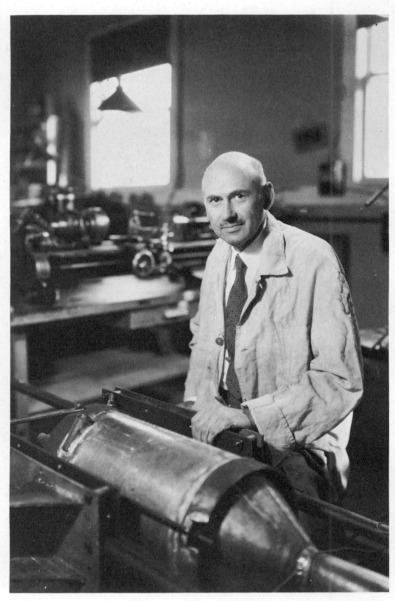

Robert Hutchings Goddard
1882–1945

ROBERT GODDARD

SPACE PIONEER

by Anne Perkins Dewey

With Illustrations

LITTLE, BROWN AND COMPANY
BOSTON
TORONTO

139348

To Marjorie Hayes

Acknowledgments

The author wishes to acknowledge with appreciation the co-operation of Mrs. Robert H. Goddard in permitting the use of her late husband's diaries and other papers; also her assistance in checking the manuscript of this book for accuracy of fact and interpretation. All the photographs and diagrams in this book have been chosen from her large collection, and are used with her kind permission.

Grateful acknowledgment is also made to the following, who have been most generous in advising the author on scientific aspects of the work: her husband, Dr. Davis R. Dewey II, President of Baird-Atomic, Inc.; Mr. A. John Gale, President of Goodrich-High Voltage Astronautics, Inc., and Dr. Daniel F. Comstock, President of Comstock, Westcott, Inc.

Robert Goddard
Space Pioneer

Dr. Goddard at blackboard, Clark University, 1924

One

One week-end morning in 1898 a muffled explosion rocked the house belonging to Nahum Goddard and his family in Boston. But there was no panic. This happened to be the third such explosion in less than a month, so it was no wonder! Whenever young Bob Goddard retired to his bedroom-laboratory to do an experiment, the family was prepared for anything.

In her sitting room, Gram merely looked up for a moment, and finding the four walls still intact, continued with her knitting.

Downstairs, Bob's parents sat at the breakfast table. They could hear the young inventor moving furniture in the room above them.

His mother sighed, and her husband looked at her sharply.

"Fanny, if Bob's experiments are upsetting you, I'll put a stop to them, right now." He put down his morning paper and pushed back his chair.

"Oh, I'm fine, really!" protested Mrs. Goddard. "I was just

thinking about finding a new maid when Annie leaves us."

"Oh, is Annie leaving?"

Mrs. Goddard laughed. "I imagine she's already packing! I must admit, today's fireworks were the loudest so far." As she said this, there was a particularly violent thump upstairs.

"Well, we'll soon find out about Annie," said Mr. Goddard. "Just ring for fresh coffee and see what happens."

After ringing twice without producing Annie, Mrs. Goddard went in search of her. The little maid was shortly discovered, tear-streaked and shaken, cowering in a broom closet.

"Oh, ma'am!" she wailed. "This time he's killed me! Oh, I'm dead, I *know* I'm dead!"

"Why, Annie, you couldn't make nearly this much noise if you were really dead, could you?" said Mrs. Goddard reasonably. "Now dry your eyes, like a good girl, and come out of the closet."

After a cup of good black tea Annie became a bit calmer, but nothing could persuade her to stay on with the Goddards. Things had never been like this where she had worked before, she sobbed, and Mrs. Goddard was sure this was true. She privately suspected that things weren't like this anywhere outside of her own household.

For the hundredth time she wondered what made Bob so different from other children. It was plain, by now, that he had inherited her own poor health, and perhaps this accounted for his being more reserved and thoughtful than most other youngsters. There wasn't much he could do besides read and think during the long weeks he often spent in bed, recovering from colds and coughs. But did this explain the burning need to know, the urge to find things out for himself?

Whatever the answer, his mother was wise enough to know that she couldn't change Bob even if she wanted to.

"Which I don't," she said aloud. "Because I like him the way he is."

"And so do I," said her husband as he helped himself to a fresh cup of coffee. "Perhaps he's inherited the unquenchable Goddard brilliance from me, and his beauty from you," he added teasingly.

"Oh, go on with you!" said his wife. "And will you for goodness' sakes look upstairs and see if Bob is really in one piece?"

Mr. Goddard found his son in the wreckage of his room, ruefully examining a bleeding knuckle cut by a piece of flying glass.

"That was a pretty noisy one, wasn't it, Pa?" said the boy a little sheepishly.

"One of your noisiest," replied Mr. Goddard as together they set about making order out of the chaos of the room.

As they worked, Bob explained that the purpose of this latest experiment had been an attempt to manufacture artificial diamonds.

"I got the idea from the science teacher at school," said Bob. "But I didn't realize the combination of oxygen and hydrogen could be so explosive."

"It's apt to be," said his father wryly.

"But it was a dandy blowup," said the boy as he dreamily pried a splinter of glass from the leg of a chair.

Not for the first time, Mr. Goddard wondered if an accidental explosion wasn't even more fun for Bob than the experiment itself.

The boy admitted it. "Of course," he said. "There's nothing like it when things go whizzing through the air the way they did today!"

A short while later, things were whizzing again, but not quite so violently as they had earlier in the day.

Bob lay on his back in a corner of the yard, aiming a homemade bow and arrows at the sky. Each arrow was wrapped with copper wire at the forward end, and each was weighted differently from the rest. Bob watched, fascinated, as the arrows leaped straight into the air, one after the other, and then fell down, wobbling pretty much in the direction he'd planned.

The last one had just fallen when he heard a startled exclamation from the far side of the yard.

His grandmother was kneeling at the flowerbed, surrounded by gardening tools.

"The strangest thing, Robby," she said. "My glasses just this minute *flew* right off my nose. Can you see them anywhere?"

Bob retrieved the glasses, as well as his arrow, which he tried to hide behind his back, but not in time.

Gram laughed. "This doesn't seem to be your day, does it?

But at least it seems you haven't been trying to fly, lately!"

"I haven't *what?*" Bob was appalled.

"I guess you were too tiny to remember," chuckled his grandmother. "But that's just what you once wanted to do."

Little five-year-old Bob had seen electricity produced by a

Family group (four generations) on steps of Maple Hill, Worcester, Mass., about 1890

Leclanché battery in his uncle's workshop. He had also found that electric sparks could be made by scuffing his feet along the carpet. Putting two and two together in his childish fashion, he decided that, by rubbing his shoe soles with zinc from one of these batteries, he could doubtless produce a mighty enough spark to propel him to the moon. He was busily en-

R. H. Goddard with his mother and father, in hammock in apple trees on grounds of Maple Hill (now 1 Tallawanda Drive), Worcester, Mass., about 1892

gaged in testing this theory, scuffling energetically up and down the sidewalk, when his mother called out that he should be careful. The experiment might work, and he would go sailing off and not be able to return! Little Bob then hid the zinc rod, and abandoned the study of space flight for some time.

"You'd have had company out there in space, though."

Bob and Gram looked up to see that Mr. Goddard had joined them. "Did I ever tell you about the old Chinese gentleman, centuries ago, who attached thirty-four firecrackers to his easy chair, lit the fuse, and was never seen on earth again? I expect he's still out there, circling round and round."

The three laughed. "But speaking of things like space flight, Bob," said Mr. Goddard, "I'd like a word with you about this book you've been reading." He held out a well-worn volume of H. G. Wells's newly published book *War of the Worlds*.

Gram gathered up her gardening things and tactfully retired to the house.

"You probably know that a lot of people are calling this book nonsense, or worse," said Mr. Goddard.

"But, Pa!" cried Bob.

"Now, hold on. You don't think it's nonsense," continued his father. "And, as a matter of fact, neither do I. I have no doubt that travel in outer space *will* be possible someday, perhaps more or less in the way Wells describes it. And you'll probably want to have something to do with it." He paused.

"But Bob!" His father's exclamation brought Bob Goddard

back from a thousand miles in space. "Haphazard experiments like today's won't launch one of those space machines Wells talks about. And marks like these in math won't help you to do any better."

To Bob's horror, Mr. Goddard produced his son's latest report card, newly arrived in the mail.

Mr. Goddard read aloud: " 'Robert masters the principles of mathematics easily, but his answers to long problems seldom include the correct solution.' "

Then, to Bob's relief, his father began to laugh.

"On the other hand," said Mr. Goddard, "I have here a letter telling me that my son recently took some examinations for entrance into the Roxbury Latin School. The headmaster expresses some puzzlement, since he hadn't any application from any Robert Goddard, and the boy was obviously unprepared."

Bob blushed. "Well," he said. "Everyone else seemed to be taking them, so I thought I'd try, just for fun. How did I do?"

"You flunked," said his father. "But," he added, shaking his head in wonder, "you beat them all in mental and written arithmetic. And that ruins my lecture on how you'll need to work on your math if you want to do anything with this space dream of yours. But it's true just the same."

Bob's father stalked off, in mock disgust, and Bob hurried away to a friend's house, calling back something about a date to send up a balloon.

While he was away from the house, his parents and Gram had a chance to discuss a serious problem concerning his future.

Mrs. Goddard had suffered from increasingly poor health for many years, and now her illness had finally been diagnosed as pulmonary tuberculosis. This meant that she would no longer be able to manage the big house in Boston. Regretfully, they had decided that the only solution was to move to Worcester. Gram owned a big farmhouse there, just outside of town, where Bob's "aunt" and "uncle" Boswell, old family friends, had been living for some time.

"The more the merrier," said Gram cheerfully, "And the country air will do Fanny a world of good."

Bob's mother was to leave for the farm right away, to be cared for there by her great-aunt, Czarina. Her husband and son and Gram would join her as soon as her husband could sell the house and his half-interest in the machine-tool factory where he worked.

"We'll make out, Fanny," said Mr. Goddard. "The important thing is for you to be well, and you will!"

"Of course I will, very soon," agreed his wife. "And think of the time Bob will have, living in the same house with his 'Uncle' George Boswell. Once those two get together again, today's excitement will look like nothing at all."

Mr. Goddard chuckled. "Remember how they captured poor crippled Granny Ward, and tested her eyesight all day long, and she couldn't get away?"

There really did seem to be a good side to the situation, Mrs. Goddard agreed.

"But, Nahum, what about school for Bob?"

Mr. Goddard thought for a minute.

"I think he can do it. I'm sure he can!"

He explained to the two women that he had had a word or two to say to Bob about his work.

"And unless I'm much mistaken, I think he's ready to pay some serious attention to math and physics. Especially if he thinks there might be a possibility of getting into a college like Worcester Tech in a few years. I think he can do it," he repeated.

Bob returned in a little while, to report a second scientific failure to add to the day's record.

He and a friend, Jim Young, had spent most of the day outside the store where Jim worked, fruitlessly trying to launch their balloon, while a chill spring rain fell upon them and their brain child. But Bob's spirits, at least, were undampened.

"Jim caught an awful cold," he said, "but I didn't. I was too excited when the thing almost worked."

Perhaps because it was spring, and the brisk March wind demanded the flying of kites, Bob had thought of launching a small balloon, attached to a line as if it were a kite. This was to be no ordinary balloon, however, since he hoped to moor it permanently in the sky over Boston! Accordingly, he and Jim had spent much of the past few weeks at the Goddards' stove, trying to make thin sheet-aluminum for the body of the balloon. This had resulted many a time in the wood fire being extinguished by molten aluminum. The recently departed Annie would come to the kitchen after her rest, expecting to find the evening meal still bubbling merrily, only to discover cold ashes and a congealed mess of food, peppered with metal spatterings.

When this part of the experiment failed, the boys managed to get hold of some ready-made sheet-aluminum, which Bob molded into pillow shape, sealing the edges with a cement of litharge and glycerin. The culmination of all this had been today's attempt to send up the balloon, filled with hydrogen. Alas, the thin aluminum was not thin enough, and the silvery pillow was too heavy to leave the ground. The boys had launched a lead balloon!

"I guess you might call it another of those 'haphazard experiments' you were talking about, Pa," said Bob. "But it was fun trying."

"Well, don't worry," said his father. "If things go as we hope, you'll know what you're doing one of these days." And he explained the plan to move to Worcester.

As they had hoped, Bob was overjoyed. Especially he seemed to welcome the challenge of earning a place at Worcester Tech. He looked forward to going on in high school and announced himself determined to get to the top of his class in math, with entrance into "Tech" as his goal.

The boy went to his room to write up his latest experiment. Characteristically, he finished his report by saying cheerfully, and with his typical spelling, "Failior crowns enterprise!"

Downstairs, Mr. Goddard turned to his wife. "Now I'm more sure than ever," he said. "If Bob says he can do it I'm certain he can."

Mrs. Goddard smiled. "Of course he can. Bob Goddard will do whatever he sets his mind to."

Gram agreed. "Just watch him!"

Two

On the day of the move to Worcester, Bob, his father, and Gram were met at the station by Ella and George Boswell. "Uncle" George was driving the horse and carriage, painted and polished.

As they rumbled around the last bend in the road up Maple Hill, a joyful chorus of soprano yapping announced to the world that the Goddards had arrived at their new home.

"We were going to sell some of the beasts even before you people decided to move in," explained George. "But Ella and I never could agree on which ones to part with. So, with the latest litter of pups, we've got fourteen of them!"

"Which makes about a dozen cockers too many, but what can you do?" sighed Ella. "George built them a nice pen, though, so they won't be underfoot."

The carriage turned into the farmyard, and from around the corner of the barn raced a small army of highly excited cocker spaniels, the little ones struggling to keep up with their elders.

Bob was delighted. "It looks as if you need some help mending fences," he laughed.

Then the kitchen door opened, and Aunt Czarina and Ma joined the welcoming committee, making their way through a sea of dogs.

"Fanny, you look just fine!" said Pa. "You've done a good job with your patient, Czarina."

The little woman beamed.

"We're going to fatten *you* up some, too, young man," she said, looking at Bob with a zealous gleam in her eye. "You may have grown a foot since last summer, but I declare, boy, you're so skinny you scarcely cast a shadow." And she bustled off upstairs to help Pa settle Gram for a rest.

In the front hall, Ma and Ella had started unpacking, chatting as they worked. Ma's voice spoke from the depths of a steamer trunk. "Bob, dear, run upstairs and see if Gram needs anything, will you?"

There was no answer.

"Bob? Well for goodness' sake. Where did that boy disappear to so fast?"

Ella called out from the closet where she was hanging outdoor clothes: "George, see if you can't find Bob."

There was silence.

"Well, we might have known they'd go off together first thing!" she laughed. "Honestly, Fanny, I don't know which of those two children is more excited about this move, your son or my husband."

True enough, the boy and his uncle were looking over "their" property like a pair of country squires, happily revisiting all the favorite spots which Bob had come to love in past visits to Maple Hill. Now that he was to live here permanently, he felt responsible for this house and land. He was full of ideas for repairs and improvements.

Behind the barn, almost hidden by a scrubby growth of swamp maple, a narrow stream made its way across the meadow. On its near bank there grew a fine old cherry tree, much overgrown and choked with dead branches.

"First we'll prune that sorry tree, before we lose it entirely," said Bob firmly. "And then we'll dig away a bit of the bank here, and set up some sort of dam a little downstream."

George failed to see how damming the stream contributed to "improvement" or "repair."

"I guess I forgot to tell you," explained Bob. "I've pretty much decided to support myself raising frogs, and this would be the perfect spot for the hatching house. It'll be about three feet long by one foot wide, and I'll paint it gray with red trim, and put in regular glass windows."

"For the frogs to see out, I suppose," said George, nodding wisely.

"For me to see in," replied Bob patiently. "And to make it look right."

He went on to describe the equipment he planned for the hatchery: water wheels, pumps, and elaborate engines, all dedicated to the development of a mighty race of Leopard frogs who would soon make a small fortune for their keeper.

As Bob went on about the wonders of the proposed hatchery, his "uncle" began to smile.

"I don't think you really want to raise frogs at all!" he said at last, when the boy stopped for breath. "I think what you want is to make the wheels turn, and the pumps pump, and never mind the frogs. But the old cherry tree certainly does need attention, so how about starting on that, and decide later whether you really want to devote your life to frogs?"

That afternoon Bob returned to the meadow, armed with a small ladder, a hatchet, and a saw. His favorite of the cockers trotted beside him.

For a while he busied himself clearing away the dead twigs, whacking at them with a hatchet to make room to attack the big branches further up. The unusually bright October sun beat down so intensely that he soon shed his heavy jacket. The black cocker basked in the sunlight, while Bob hiked himself up into the tree and started to saw on the stoutest of the dead limbs.

The little saw made slow progress, but after a long time of steady work there was a creak, followed by a satisfying crack, and the old limb gave way.

"Timber!" cried Bob as it crashed earthward, and the sleepy cocker leaped out of the way in the nick of time.

Pleased with himself, Bob hung the saw on a twig and leaned back to rest, hooking his arms around the smooth tree trunk behind him.

He sighed contentedly. It occurred to him that this was one of those wonderful days when everything was just right:

the move to Maple Hill, the cockers, the tree, the weather. Everything was perfect.

The honey-colored meadows, criss-crossed with ancient stone walls, seemed to roll forever into the distance, and in the crystal autumn air he thought he could see clear to the next town.

He hugged himself with sheer pleasure, risking a tumble.

"Today I could do *anything*," he said aloud. "The sky's the limit!" Then he looked up into the limitless blue October sky.

"The sky's the limit?" he repeated softly. "Who says so? Why should it be? There's a *lot* up there beyond the blue part; Venus, and Mars, and a trillion others. No, the sky is *not* the limit."

Then in his mind's eye Bob saw his homemade copper-bound arrows, streaking skyward, only to tumble awkwardly back to earth, end over end. It was obvious that to reach any real distance into that tantalizing blue, a projectile would need many times the "push" that had launched the arrows from the bow.

Bob had read about centrifugal force. Now he wondered if it might not give him the needed thrust, if only on a small scale.

The principle of this force can be demonstrated in this way: If you take a bucket of water, and swing it in a vertical circle, the water won't spill out even when the open end is down. This is because centrifugal force is working to push the water against the bottom of the bucket. This is despite the force of gravity, which otherwise would empty the bucket in an instant. Just stop swinging it, suddenly, and you will see gravity have its way! You might say that the water is "projected," just as Bob hoped to project an object into the atmosphere—or even beyond it.

Another example of this principle can be seen when you tie a string around a stone, and, holding the free end, whirl the stone in a circle around your head. As long as you hold fast to the string and keep swinging, the stone will travel in a circle. But as soon as you let go it will take off like a shot, propelled by its own momentum. Of course, the faster you swing the farther the stone will fly before it yields to the force of gravity and falls.

This was the type of propulsion Bob had in mind that October afternoon, but suspecting that it too might prove to be a fairly limited method, he looked forward more than ever to starting school again. Surely he would find some of the answers when he could work in a real laboratory.

Unhappily, it soon turned out that Bob would have to postpone going to school. The Goddards' luck was surely at a low ebb: Ma was sick again, Gram was feeling poorly, and now Bob himself was suffering from a stomach trouble he'd had off and on for most of his life.

Seeing the boy drooping over his plate one evening, unable to touch his food, Aunt Czarina put him to bed, and Pa sent for Dr. White.

"It's the same old story," the doctor told Bob's father. "And there's something very wrong when a youngster has siege after siege of this sort of thing. I think the time has come to operate, and see if we can't straighten him out once and for all."

"How serious an operation would it be?" asked Mr. Goddard.

"Very serious. It would be long and dangerous."

"And the alternative?"

"Rest, rest, and more rest, for a long while," replied the doctor gravely. "Then limited activity for some time after that."

The two men talked a while longer. Then Dr. White went away, leaving Pa with a hard decision to make. He couldn't make it alone.

The elder members of the family talked together in Ma's room, and all agreed that a program of rest would be better than the risk of a major operation.

"Poor old Bob," sighed George Boswell. "But one thing's certain; nothing on earth is going to keep that mind of his out of action. It just can't be done."

It was Mr. Goddard's gloomy task to break the news to Bob that he would not, after all, be able to start school.

"But there's a good side to this," he told the boy. "Dr. White tells me the town is planning to put up a new high school just down at Richards and Main Streets." He went on to explain that the plans for the school included bringing in the very best teachers from all over the city. Moreover, the school board proposed a system which would allow an able student to specialize, and get extra help in his favorite subject. "That sounds made to order for the projects you have in mind, doesn't it?" said Mr. Goddard.

Bob was not quite convinced that this particular cloud had as silvery a lining as his father would have him believe.

"How long?" he asked suspiciously.

"Oh, well," said Pa vaguely, "I should think by the time South High is ready for you, you'll be ready for South High."

"I said 'How long?', Pa."

His father sighed. "I guess as much as two years, son," he admitted.

"*Two years!*" screamed Bob. "Glory! In two years I'll be nineteen years old! Nineteen, and just starting my second year of high school, for heaven's sake—*Grampa* Goddard." Disgusted, he plunged under the covers to the bottom of the bed. But a few seconds later his rumpled head popped out.

"Pa, will someone go to the library for me tomorrow? I'll need something on engineering drawing, the *Scientific American, Forest and Stream,* and some others. And some stuff from the hardware store for models."

"I'll do it myself," said Mr. Goddard.

"Uncle" George, who had just stopped in to say good night, winked at Pa.

"What did I tell you?" he said.

In no time at all, the supposed sickroom began to look like a combination science library and workshop. The floor, the bedside table, and the bed itself were piled high with books, as well as a number of models in various stages of completion. George Boswell soon learned that when he needed a tool from his workshop, he might just as well look first in Bob's room!

Bob's idea of flight into space was uppermost in his mind, but he still thought of the hatchery as a means of supporting himself. The equipment for launching a rocket might turn out to be expensive.

A wondrous assortment of gadgetry began to take shape on the drawing board, and sometimes in model form as well. But by the end of the following summer Bob was still not allowed to do the wet work of installing the hatchery at the stream. So he set the project aside, not too reluctantly, and turned his thoughts once more to the dream of flight which had occurred to him almost a year before. He still liked the idea of propulsion by centrifugal force.

After a number of days of tinkering, he invited the family to a demonstration. The audience warily arranged itself in the doorway—so as to be out of the path of this flight, whatever it might be. The inventor sat cross-legged on his bed behind his apparatus.

"First I'll get this horizontal axis rotating," Bob explained.

" 'Horizontal axis,' indeed!" Aunt Czarina whispered. "That's a curtain rod from the guest bedroom."

"I was saying," continued the inventor, "that I intend to rotate this axle at high speed so as to spin the weight at the end of this string."

"The clock pendulum!" gasped Aunt Czarina.

"So that," continued Bob, "when the weight gets going

fast enough, I can release it at the top of its circle and let it rip. It should go like anything."

"*Where* will it go?" asked Ma.

Bob pointed to the ceiling, where he had thoughtfully nailed a strip of old blanket to protect the plaster.

"I expect the missile to reach the altitude of that blanket, and if it weren't for the foolish ceiling it would just go and go."

So saying, he set the machine going, and because of a clever arrangement of homemade ball-bearings, it did work up considerable speed. But there had been a slight miscalculation. At the dramatic moment for take-off, Bob touched the string with a razor blade, and at this instant the projectile was catapulted, not toward the ceiling, but in a beeline flight to and through the bedroom window, which was not open!

The housewives sighed, and Aunt Czarina hustled off to fetch a broom and dustpan.

"It isn't *possible,*" wailed Bob. He shuffled frantically through the mountain of notes at his bedside. "Here! Newton's law says for every action there's an opposite reaction. The string was holding the weight *back;* so when I cut the string, the projectile ought to have flown in the *opposite* direction: straight up."

"But Bob," said Pa, "Newton also has a law which says that a moving body will continue in its direction of motion *unless it's subjected to an external force.* You *removed* an 'external force,' when you cut the string. At the instant you did that, the weight was trying to move horizontally, toward the window. If you'd released it exactly halfway up the circle, it would have done what you wanted."

"Well, really, Nahum," said Aunt Czarina. "If you knew all along it wouldn't work, may I ask why you didn't say so before that window got broken?"

"We learn by doing," replied Pa. Then he took out pencil and paper. The result of his calculations was that Bob realized that a centrifugal machine capable of enough thrust to get a missile beyond the earth's atmosphere, and thus beyond the force of gravity, would have to be a mighty thing indeed.

"Why, even a *tiny* rocket would have to be thrown off from the earth at several miles per second, just to keep going that far," marveled Bob.

It would be many years before he worked out exactly how much speed was needed. For the moment, he abandoned centrifugal force as a means of propulsion.

But Bob was far from discouraged. There was more than one way to skin a cat, he said, and settled back in bed to reread a set of books called "Cassell's Popular Educator." He was still sure that the chapter on Newton's laws held somewhere the clue to the problem of reaching outer space.

Though at first two years of waiting had sounded like an eternity, the search for this clue helped to make the time pass quickly.

He soon came to know Newton's three all-important laws backward and forward. He tested them with models as best

he could, and laughed when he read that the great scientist
had been considered a poor student because *he* devoted so
much time to models and mechanical devices.

But this could no longer be said of Bob himself. His weak-
est point, math, was gaining strength as he delved into algebra
and trigonometry.

Then, after a while, he was able to take a special part-time
course at business college to improve his handwriting and
spelling.

On the way to and from the class he often took a detour
past the fast-growing new school building. As the classrooms
took shape it was fun to guess which would be his when the
time came.

Then, in the fall of 1901, the finished building was dedicated. Bob and Gram were there to hear the speechmaking.
And a few days later he was at school again—ready for the adventure, armed with new books and new ideas.

Three

"Got a problem? Whatever it is, Bob Goddard will solve it for you with a math formula."

It didn't take long for Robert Goddard to earn this reputation, and it kept him busy. Whenever any sort of committee was formed, the boy who shortly before had been "too frail" to go to school was sure to be on it.

"How did it go today?" asked Gram one afternoon.

Bob made his usual reply. "Pretty fair. Is there anything to eat?"

His grandmother gave him fruit and a glass of milk.

"Only 'pretty fair'?"

"Well, we had the class elections, and that was interesting. We've got a new president and vice-president."

"Anybody I know?"

"Uh-huh," said Bob, grinning around a faceful of apple. "The vice-president is me."

Gram was pleased. "And you thought you'd be Grandpa Goddard, too old for all the others. Well, well."

"Oh," said Bob, "They probably respect my old gray head."
He scooped up his books and bounded up the stairs, two at a
time.

What with his class offices, editing the school paper, singing
and acting in all the shows, *and* serving as class pianist, it
seems a wonder that there was any time left for study. But
Bob thought of these school years as steppingstones to the
space dream.

The courses were all he had hoped they would be. He was
able to get special help in physics, which he wanted, and in
math, which he knew he needed. He bolstered his own interest in math by doing a painstaking notebook of original
geometric propositions. He found that the challenge made it
a pleasure to think about geometry, and as this new kind of
logic unfolded he wondered that he had ever thought it a bore.

And still, there was time left over for reading and experimenting at home.

In reading about anything and everything to do with science, Bob came to realize that no field of science stands alone.
Physics calls upon chemistry, and vice versa. Astronomy needs
meteorology, and engineering depends upon mathematics. To
his surprise he found on reading a book on physiology that
even the study of anatomy might help him in his reach for
high altitudes.

The human body, he learned, depends upon a tiny struc-
ture in the inner ear for its sense of balance. This led him to

wonder how a bird maintains its balance while in flight, and
he discovered that in birds, also, balancing is automatic because of this system of semicircular canals. These tiny, hair-
like tubes, filled with fluid, are imbedded in the bone of the
skull. The three tubes lie at right angles to one another.
Through delicate nerve endings, each tube directs the bird's
flight movements in the plane on which the tube lies.

He tried to construct a mechanical version of this system,
looking ahead to the day when a rocket would need a balancing device to tell it whether it was on course. But—he soon
found out how hard it was to duplicate the work of nature.
The model was a failure, but he had learned a little more
about the problems of flight.

Then one day he came upon a different idea for control
during flight, when he was actually thinking of quite another
thing—of how to *propel* a rocket. He happened to remember
the almost uncanny behavior of a childhood toy, a gyroscope
top. A gyroscope is a top which "wants" to do what it sets out
to do. In other words, if it is once sent spinning and moving
in a given direction, in a given position, and on a given plane,
it will "object" if you try to re-direct it. Set such a top spinning
with a mighty twist, and it will make its way merrily around
the rim of a glass or up or down any surface where you choose
to set it going. If you try to push it over, or up, or down, and
if your original twist was "mighty" enough, it will right itself
in its determined fashion and carry on as before.

Bob's first thought was to use this stubborn resistance in
some way as a force for propelling a rocket. But this proved

impractical: the force was too tiny to be of use to even a very small model rocket. Nevertheless, he carefully recorded the experiment in his notebook.

"Why do that?" asked a friend who had dropped in to see what Bob was up to. "If the thing doesn't work, what's the use in writing it up?"

"Because it's just as important to know what won't work as it is to find out what will," Bob explained. "Besides, in every 'no good' experiment there just might be the germ of a good idea. Nothing gets wasted, this way."

True enough, the germ of a very good idea emerged from this early work with the gyroscope.

Why wouldn't a combination of these devices, perhaps set up at right angles to one another the way the semicircular canals are arranged, have a different kind of usefulness? It might be used in a rocket to "report" conditions which were trying to push the gyros, and hence the rocket itself, off course. Perhaps, with proper wiring, the resistance would be strong enough to influence a mechanism for putting the rocket back on course.

But until a rocket could actually be launched it wasn't practical to spend too much time wondering how to guide it. Bob filed the idea away with other thoughts not to be wasted.

After a while Bob came to realize that his space dream set him a little apart from the other students. His friends were loyal, but none had his vision, and few could listen to his ideas without becoming hopelessly baffled, try as they might.

Because of his fascination with space, he wrote most of his English themes on such subjects as the motion of stars, and on such questions as whether Mars had ever been inhabited, or could be again. He explained that by analyzing the kind of light given off by a star it was possible to tell what substances were giving off the light. The element carbon had been found in light reflected from Mars, and since carbon is necessary to living things, Bob insisted that life might well have existed there at one time.

"Dear old Bob," said his classmates when he read this theme in assembly. "If he has his way, we'll hold our twenty-fifth reunion on Mars!"

Echoes of these remarks reached Bob. In self-defense he wrote another essay, which his teacher graded A as usual. He was asked to read it aloud.

"Even today," read Bob, eying his particular critics severely, "when any radical scientific theory is advanced, whether it is right or wrong, there are multitudes of people, many of whom scarcely know what the theory is, that always rise to cry it down."

He grinned when more than one listener squirmed.

"If Robert Fulton had listened to the public for an instant," continued the speaker, "he would have thrown his plans away and asked his friends never to mention the word 'steamboat.' "

"Miriam, dare we mention the word 'rocket' to Bob?" giggled a girl in the audience to her neighbor.

"Hush!" replied her friend. "He's worth listening to."

"Well, you ought to know!" hissed the other girl. At a withering glance from Miriam, she subsided.

Meanwhile, the speaker was finishing his talk with another of his favorite ideas.

"The best plan for all of us to follow," he read, "is to leave our researches and investigations until knowledge and experience are attained, after which our work will either be crowned with success or buried once and for all as an impossibility."

"There, what did I tell you?" said Miriam as the girls went off to their next class. "Bob Goddard is *very practical*."

Early in his senior year at school, Bob had a chance to prove that he was indeed practical—and diplomatic besides. He had been chosen to head the senior class banquet committee, but what was supposed to be a sentimental occasion seemed to be developing into open warfare.

It so happened that the girls fancied themselves star athletes, having won a basketball championship. Perhaps their success went to their heads, for some were soon heard to grumble about the boys' performance in sports, which had not been spectacular. They let it be known that the boys were absolutely hopeless, and had spoiled an otherwise brilliant class record.

The boys muttered that they had "a pretty poor crowd of girls."

This caused the girls to sulk and recall a number of other grievances.

"What about all the husking bees and sleigh rides their

silly entertainment committee talked about for four years?" they grumbled. "We never had *one.*"

Hearing this, the boys insisted they'd never been able to find a chaperone willing to risk life or limb for those girls.

Even loyal Miriam bridled at this, half-agreeing with her friends, who said, "We've got a pretty poor crowd of boys!"

By the time final arrangements were to be made for the banquet, there was precious little class spirit left to celebrate. The class of 1904 was completely divided, with its president, Bob Goddard, uneasily trying to restore peace.

For some days the boys were smug and mysterious, and the girls increasingly uneasy and suspicious.

An all-male meeting was held, and the girls heard that a petition of some sort was being signed. Their president's face, when he was asked about this, was a picture of guilt. Reluctantly, Bob admitted that the object of the paper was to get permission from the school principal to have a banquet without the presence of the young ladies.

At her friends' insistence, Miriam pled with him and Bob changed his stand. He appealed to the boys' sense of chivalry, explaining that the poor girls, most of them, had no sense at all and so weren't responsible for their behavior.

By the end of the year all was once more serene between the girls and the boys, and Miriam even went so far as to say "I think so," when Bob questioned her about their future plans.

At graduation, Bob, the class orator, gave a speech which he called "On Taking Things for Granted." He closed with the thought that it is unwise to say that a new idea is impossible because, as he said, "The dream of yesterday is the hope of today and the reality of tomorrow."

But his own dream did not look very rosy at the moment. He had learned enough physics to know that many of his ideas wouldn't work.

He had a set of models, most of which didn't work either. Despite his philosophy about wasting nothing, he one day burned all of them, and all the notes he could find, in the little wood stove in the dining room.

But, happily, the dream would not "down," and within two months he found himself making notes on further suggestions. For even though he reasoned with himself that the space dream was impossible, there was something inside him which simply would not stop working on the problem.

He bought a set of green cloth notebooks in which he was to record his every thought and calculation on the space idea for the next ten years. These books would contain the beginnings of the Goddard rocket, as well as ideas on jet propulsion, the use of solar energy, the possible usefulness of atomic energy, and many other ideas far in advance of the time in which they were written. Some of them became reality during Bob Goddard's lifetime; others have taken actual form only recently.

During the summer following high school graduation, Bob talked with people at Worcester Tech about getting a scholarship there for the coming year. His mother's medical expenses were a great burden on the family finances, so some such arrangement would be necessary if he was to have his chance at college. His performance at school had certainly earned it. But many other hard-working young men were applying for scholarships.

It was Gram who helped swing the decision in his favor. When "Madam Goddard," as she was known in the community, said something should be done, it was usually done!

The four years at Tech were quite a contrast to the fairly carefree days at high school. This was a world of grown men struggling through various difficult courses in science. Those who did not struggle successfully soon fell by the wayside. When exams came around, Tech boys could be heard gloomily conjugating the classic fractured verbs: *flunk, flunkeri, faculti, fireus,* and *examini, flunkeri, suspendi, expulsum.*

Though never close to the danger of *faculti, fireus,* being well protected by his A average, Bob was often discouraged at first. Some of his ideas were so advanced that his physics professor, far-seeing as he himself was, felt compelled to pull his brilliant student back down to earth.

Bob wrote a paper on the utilization of atomic energy. He prophesied that energy from radioactive substances would eventually power rockets in interplanetary space. Thus he anticipated not only rocket flight, but the constructive use of the power of the atom. But shortly after handing in this paper, he had to write in his diary that Dr. Duff had said the idea was of no use. A few days later the diary records the flat statement: "Space navigation is a physical impossibility."

Luckily the discouragement was only temporary, and once more his dream would not "down."

He continued to think and write on all aspects of his favorite subject. In 1907, at the end of his junior year at Tech, the *Scientific American* accepted and printed his article on the use of the gyroscope for balancing airplanes.

In the year following his graduation the same magazine printed a condensed version of one of his most extreme college themes, which he had called "Traveling in 1950." It was published as part of an unsigned editorial, "The Limit of Rapid Transit." In it he suggested the possibility of rapid travel in air-sealed cars magnetically suspended in a tremendous vacuum tube or tunnel. The cars would have no contact with a roadbed or rail, and would be propelled by the action of magnets in the walls of both car and tunnel. A positive magnetic field would draw the car forward; when it passed this source, the field would change from attraction to repulsion. The magnets behind would be "pushing," while those ahead "pulled"! It was an ingenious idea, and while it hadn't much to do with rockets, it was fun to think about.

It was somewhat optimistic to think that we would be ready for this means of travel as early as 1950. But if the idea works out, as so many of Dr. Goddard's "impossible" ideas have, our grandchildren may one day travel this way, hurtling lickety-split from city to city and coast to coast.

The same year that saw the publication of this article found Bob, a graduate now, back on the Tech campus. He was giving the lectures instead of listening to them, though this was not quite what he had planned. He had hoped to go directly into graduate work at Clark University, in Worcester, where study for his doctor's degree would be a big step toward realizing his space dream. Use of the laboratories there would be a tremendous help, too.

"But we just can't do it, Bob," said his father. Mr. Goddard showed his son the pile of doctors' bills for Ma.

Gram had nothing to spare, either, from the tiny pension of a Civil War widow. "I'm sorry, Rob," she said.

So there would be a year of teaching at Tech to save money for further study.

Bob threw himself into his new career with great energy, and found he enjoyed it. His students did, too!

He remembered vividly the agony of being asked a question in class and being expected to answer before having time to gather his wits. So he developed a habit which made him beloved by all his pupils throughout his years of teaching. He would pose a question to a student, and if the boy hesitated, he would stroll casually to the window. There he would stand, his back to the room, softly whistling a tune which came to be well-known to the class. After one or two renditions of "The Rocky Road to Dublin," sometimes interspersed with a thoughtful re-phrasing of the question, the student usually relaxed and came up with the answer. For this they forgave him his occasional jokes at their expense.

Later, when he was working with solid fuels for propelling rockets, one particular prank was his delight.

He would hold up what looked like a strand of uncooked spaghetti. "This," he would explain, "is the latest rocket propellant"—and he would calmly light one end with a match, while the class cringed, waiting for an explosion. As the stick of fuel burned quietly and steadily, the lecturer would remark, "Slow and steady wins the game."

Early in their college years, hers at Smith and his at Worcester Tech, Bob's understanding with Miriam became a definite engagement. She was wearing his ring and his fraternity pin.

But as time went on he found that she was beginning to be doubtful about the long years that lay ahead if Bob were to follow his persistent dream.

"Getting your doctor's degree will take forever, at this rate," she had said when he found he must postpone study and take a teaching job. "Perhaps you should just keep on teaching when you graduate and give up this idea of the degree. We could marry as early as next spring if you were earning a regular salary."

Bob had been horrified. He was willing to teach, because a man had to make a living. But give up the idea of graduate work? Not for a minute. This would be giving up access to the important university laboratories he needed to use.

He tried hard to explain, but Miriam went on to talk excitedly about spending the summer in Europe after her college graduation, shopping for linens and a wedding dress for the following spring.

Bob was even more confused when she wrote from college that she was considering studying towards a degree in zoology while she was in Europe.

"Now she's thinking about a career as well as marriage," Bob had confided unhappily to his father. Or was it "instead of"? He was completely muddled, and only wished she would make up her mind.

He had put this latest letter aside and stamped off for a walk to get his mind on other things. "Women!" he growled as he marched out of the house.

It was a fine fall day, and after a long walk from home to the Tech campus he could hear shouts of "Yea, Tech! Good old 1908!"

"You'd think no one had anything more important than *football* to think about," he grumbled to himself. But was it actually possible that the Varsity *had* won a game? A classroom door burst open, and he found himself swept off with a crowd of Tech men, all rushing down to the field. They found the "Techs" jubilant, and the goal posts tumbling under the onslaught of a horde of ecstatic freshmen.

"This calls for a celebration!" someone cried. "We ought to fly a banner, or something, from the top of Boynton Hall!"

Suddenly the world looked rosier.

"That's right!" Bob agreed. "We need a symbol of the occasion." He looked about him, and his inventive eye was caught by what looked like a worthy emblem for the victorious '08's. A new clothing firm had set up an enormous metal sign in the form of a life-sized elephant with the words WATCH US GROW printed on its side.

A pot of black paint, a brush, and some bold brushwork were all that were needed to change the U to an 0, and the S to a wobbly 8. WATCH 08 GROW was now the cry, and the new class mascot was straightway spirited to a precarious perch atop Boynton Hall.

Bob had come home that evening to report that he had had a most refreshing day. For the time being the shaky engagement was forgotten.

But in the course of the next two years the situation became even shakier. The summer trip to Europe following Miriam's college graduation stretched out to a year. Soon after that, when Bob had finished his year of teaching and was at last at Clark doing graduate work, the issue was definitely closed. The two decided that they were headed in opposite directions, and Miriam returned Bob's letters, his pin, and his ring.

"It seems funny," he said to Gram. "The people at Clark have kept telling me that I should have special study in Europe to go on with my research. I haven't been able to go, but Miriam has. And she's come back a different person."

He sighed. "Oh, well. The chances are it would have been the same if *I'd* been the one to go. Or we might have married earlier and then *both* changed, when it was too late to turn back."

Gram said nothing. She knew that the right girl for Bob Goddard would have to be as dedicated to the space dream as he himself was.

Bob knew this, too, but nevertheless the broken engagement was a disappointment. For the next few months he worked even harder towards the final exams for his doctor's degree.

The evening after the long day of oral examination he dragged himself home, having no idea of what he had said during the hours of questioning, or how his answers had been received.

"For all I know I may have just babbled nonsense at them!" he told his grandmother.

But very soon the doorbell rang, and it rang again and again throughout the evening. One after another, the men who had examined him, and others who had heard rumors about his performance, dropped in to call.

"You did yourself proud, and everyone connected with you!" said one.

"A brilliant exam. One of the best we've had," was another comment. "I was proud to know one of my students could have such a grasp of his subject."

The praise went on and on, but by the time Gram closed the door behind the last caller, her grandson was fast asleep in his chair.

"Dr. Goddard," she whispered.

Bob slept on.

"Dr. Goddard!" she called at the top of her voice.

Bob Goddard woke with a start. "Why, that's me!" he cried. Grinning sleepily he stumbled upstairs, where he threw himself on his bed and was asleep in an instant.

Four

It took most of the summer to recover from the grueling months that had preceded that day of examinations. Dr. Goddard was a weary man. He was a little discouraged, too. Whatever was the use of this elegant new degree if he couldn't find a good job with a good salary? He wanted particularly to work at Clark University, where he knew he would be among people who felt that his experimental work was important. Other universities were offering him highly-paid positions, but he doubted if many would have this understanding.

However, the president of Clark was able to offer him a year as an "Honorary Fellow in Physics," with no salary.

"I'm sorry about the money part, Bob," he said. "But at least the laboratory will be all yours."

Dr. Goddard accepted in an instant. He and Gram would simply muddle through on her pension and what was left of his savings from the year of teaching, though these were beginning to be stretched pretty thin.

The two were very much on their own, now. The household had dwindled to just Gram and himself in recent years, as the Boswells and his parents had established new homes in the neighborhood. His mother was too ill to have the care of Gram, so the old lady had remained at Maple Hill with her grandson to keep her company. They didn't live in luxury, but they made out nicely and enjoyed one another's company very much.

During this year at Clark Dr. Goddard made a number of experiments with electricity, studying the behavior of tiny particles, or electrons, when exposed to electric fields. When he heard that there would soon be an important scientific meeting at Harvard, it occurred to him that he might read a paper there on one of these experiments.

"That's what you need to do, if you want to get people interested in your research," Dr. Goddard explained to Gram. "Publish whatever you can, and talk, talk about it wherever someone will listen."

Gram thought this was a sensible idea, but she wondered if her grandson wasn't forgetting something.

"How about the rocket?" she pleaded. "What do those electron things have to do with *rockets?*"

Dr. Goddard explained that his work with electrons would indeed be useful to his rocket idea. It all went back to the rule *For every action there is an equal and opposite reaction.*

In a device called a cathode ray tube, he was trying to show that he could get a backward force, or reaction, from a beam of electrons speeded up by electricity. And now he was trying to reassure Gram that it all related to the rocket dream, and his brain child was *not* forgotten.

When she looked completely confused, and a little cross, Dr. Goddard thought for a moment.

"Look," he said. "A fireman holding a fire hose nozzle has to react, or fight back against, the force of a high-speed stream of water leaving the nozzle. Right?"

Gram nodded.

"All right," continued Dr. Goddard. "In my experiment I'm trying to measure this same kind of force: the backward force of electrically charged particles traveling in a vacuum."

"You didn't say anything before about a vacuum," complained Gram.

"If I didn't use a vacuum tube there'd be air molecules messing up the flight of the electrons. It would be like trying to throw a tennis ball through a pile of rocks."

But Gram persisted. "I don't believe this has a *thing* to do with the rocket," she said stubbornly. "Robby, I believe you've given up!"

He thought to himself that if he could explain this to his grandmother, he could teach anybody anything.

"For one thing," he went on patiently, "a device for accelerating electrons would be good for propelling a rocket. Imagine the speed of a stream of electrons bursting out of a rocket nozzle! And the motor could be relatively small, so it wouldn't have a lot of its own weight to push as well as the weight of the rocket. And for another thing, any study of electrical phenomena in a vacuum is valuable. When once a rocket gets thirty miles up, it will be flying in a virtual vacuum."

Whether or not Gram understood completely, she was satisfied. She was sure the American Physical Society would learn a great deal from her grandson's speech.

Two weeks before the meeting Dr. Goddard sent off an abstract of his proposed talk to the chairman. Afterward he repeated his experiment and found out to his dismay that he could not achieve the same result a second time.

Since working at Clark he had come to know another young physicist, a student named Stimson. "Stim" was horrified when he learned of his friend's dilemma. Was this the sane, methodical Bob Goddard he thought he knew?

Bob half-hoped the American Physical Society would say, "No thank you, Dr. Goddard."

But the abstract was enthusiastically accepted. There was no turning back now.

With Stim's help Dr. Goddard started all over again on another experiment. If it were to fail, Dr. Goddard was prepared to go to the meeting and take the consequences.

Miraculously the new experiment worked, and it worked again and again throughout the long night of testing.

It was dawn when Stim left the laboratory.

Dr. Goddard settled down to work feverishly on the preparation of his speech.

Bleary-eyed, he delivered the talk a few hours later. The

audience was impressed, but the secretary of the Society, who had accepted the original outline, was puzzled.

"It was a fine paper, Goddard," he said, "but it didn't sound quite like the abstract."

"Small wonder, sir," Dr. Goddard replied sheepishly, and escaped into the audience. This had been a lesson, and a good one!

But luck was with him, and the close call turned out very well. Before he could make his weary way home, half a dozen scientists had stopped him to praise his presentation. Some made offers of teaching positions for the coming fall. One suggestion in particular sounded like just what he wanted.

"I've got a job at Princeton!" he told Gram when he got back.

"I'm not surprised," said Gram calmly.

There was much to be done in the few months before starting his new job. He planned, once he got there, to get on with the problem of finding an efficient fuel for a rocket motor. But loose ends must be tied up first. Out came the green notebooks, so that ideas that would be useful to the rocket would be ready when needed.

One of these ideas was the theory of the multi-stage rocket, which has proved thus far to be the best solution to the problem of lifting the mighty weight of a rocket and then keeping its "pay load" in flight.

The problem would be most difficult at the moment of

take-off. A tremendous bulk must be propelled upward from an absolute standstill. This requires a great deal of apparatus which in itself adds a burden to the flying rocket. Without this extra weight it would make far better headway. The solution seemed to be to drop off this dead weight, once it had served its purpose; then let a second, much smaller motor be started, to drop off in its turn at an even greater altitude. In this way two purposes would be served: the high speed already achieved by a large motor could be maintained by a smaller one; secondly, upon reaching a high altitude, the thin air or near-vacuum would offer little resistance to the flight of the remaining part of the rocket, the instrument-carrying business end.

Dr. Goddard never saw a rocket of this type, but he was issued a patent on the idea in 1914. All of our rockets—like the Atlas, Thor, and Jupiter—operate on this principle.

There was another loose end which Dr. Goddard was hurrying to tie up in this summer of 1911. It was an idea for a motor for operating a rocket, to be run on energy supplied by the heat of the sun. This solar energy motor had occurred to him while he was still a student at Worcester Tech; and though it was to prove yet another of his many inventions which he never saw in use, every man-made satellite now operating uses solar energy.

The green notebooks' entries for January of 1908 had suggested that heat from the sun be used to vaporize a liquid, the vapor to drive a turbine, and the turbine to drive

a generator making electricity for use in a device for expell-
ing electrically charged particles.

This method of propulsion is now known as "ion propulsion," and is the subject of much interest and research.

These entries had been the culmination of some months
of speculation. And in the previous year, an outgrowth of
Dr. Goddard's beginning interest in solar energy had been an
article discussing the possibility of using radioactivity to supply
sufficient energy for rocket propulsion. He called the paper
"On the Possibility of Navigating Interplanetary Space," and
submitted it to *Popular Astronomy*. The article was rejected,
the editor's comment being, "The impossibility of ever doing
it is so certain. . . ." This was an understandable dismissal
of a glimpse into the atomic age, still decades away.

By the end of the summer of 1911 these and the other
ideas accumulated in the green notebooks were up to date
and in order. It was time to pack up for the move to
Princeton.

There was only one problem, and Dr. Goddard and Gram
were both worrying about it, though neither said anything
to the other. Gram saw that her grandson was looking frail
and tired, while Dr. Goddard was concerned about leaving
the old woman alone on Maple Hill.

He was surprised one day to find his grandmother sorting
and packing her own things.

"I didn't know you were planning a trip," he said.

"Why, indeed I am," she replied firmly. "I'm going to
Princeton."

"But, Gram—"

"Don't 'but' me, Robert Goddard. Were you going to leave an old woman alone and helpless in this great house?"

"You're no more helpless than I am," he insisted, "but I did think I'd get you a housekeeper, just for company."

"Housekeeper, nonsense!" snorted Gram. "We couldn't begin to afford it."

Dr. Goddard knew this was true enough, and he was secretly relieved that he would be able to look after her himself.

Gram got on with her packing, well pleased with herself. She had a strong feeling that this grandson of hers, who could become so absorbed in a laboratory problem that he hardly took time to eat a meal, would need some watching.

Young Dr. Goddard could look after the rocket problem; *she* would look after Dr. Goddard.

They took rooms near the university. Dr. Goddard found Princeton, with its spacious campus of old trees, a most delightful place to work, and he was overjoyed with the laboratory which had been assigned to him. Moreover, he discovered to his delight that he would not have teaching duties after all, and could devote his days to laboratory work.

To Gram's alarm he became so enthusiastic that most of his nights were spent in the laboratory, also.

"You're burning the candle at both ends, Rob," she warned. But she might just as well have tried to tell a child not to play with a favorite toy.

During the day he worked on developing the electrical

experiment which had first interested Princeton in his work. He was trying to measure the force of an electric current produced in a wire by the magnetic field of a generator. Soon he was able to give a successful demonstration of a mechanical force from this displacement field, and the men at Princeton were impressed.

Nighttime was his own, to do what he wanted. Of course what he wanted was to get right back to the laboratory and wrestle with the rocket problem. In these cherished after-hours he worked on the theory of rocket propulsion with smokeless powder as well as with different combinations of liquid hydrogen and oxygen, looking for the most efficient possible rocket fuel. His calculations showed him that he could expect 50 per cent efficiency with these last fuels, which pleased him. This may sound as if the fuel combination was only half successful, but when you consider that an automobile uses less than 20 per cent of its fuel efficiently, wasting the rest in escaping exhaust, you can see why Dr. Goddard was quite satisfied.

The daytime laboratory work involved a number of delicate experiments. The doors and windows, even the keyholes, had to be sealed, because the precise measurements he was making could be thrown off by the slightest current of air or change in air temperature. Further, the sulphurous fumes from the gas generator with which he was working were very irritating to breathe. It was not surprising that he soon developed a racking cough, and couldn't seem to shake it.

Gram kept her fingers crossed, hoping that her grandson

would not work himself into a really serious illness before Easter vacation came, when he could rest. As it turned out, the two got back to Worcester in the nick of time. Dr. Goddard was promptly put to bed with a raging fever, in the so-called "hospital room" of his parents' new house. This was the room where his mother had had to spend so much of her time, fighting her own battle with tuberculosis. She was heartbroken when the doctor confirmed her suspicion that her son, too, had contracted what was then called "galloping consumption," because of the cruel speed with which the disease could carry off its victims.

When Dr. Goddard grew worse, exhausted by incessant coughing, the doctors told his family that he had no more than two weeks to live. But they had counted without their patient's fantastic will to survive.

"There's so much to be done!" he whispered to Gram. "I can't quit now!"

Gradually, but so painfully, he began to get well. Fortunately his stubborn nature rejected the tuberculosis "cures" which were fashionable then. He would *not* sleep out of doors in the damp March air. He would *not* splash his chest with ice water, as his frail mother had been forced to do. And, above all, he would *not* give up thinking about his space dream, though the doctors assured him such mental effort would be fatal. It was some time before the nurse discovered the notes he was hiding under his mattress, and by then he had proved his point. With something important to live for, he had lived.

"This is all very well," said the doctor sternly, "But you're far from being out of danger. Disobey all my other rules if you like, but please remember this one: avoid excitement at all costs."

The patient laughed wearily. Excitement? All alone in this little room, with no visitors allowed? Small chance. He'd likely die of boredom first.

That night the thunderstorm to end all thunderstorms descended on the neighborhood. The house echoed with the rolling boom of thunder; the "hospital room" was alight with the glare of one lightning flash after another. Tree branches crashed to the ground, barely missing the house.

Then, looking out the window towards Maple Hill, Dr. Goddard watched with horror as an entire building suddenly took fire.

"Gram!" he cried, struggling to get out of bed. In a moment his father was beside him, gently pressing him back against the pillows.

"There, Bob," he soothed. "It wasn't Gram's house. Sleep, now!"

Sleep he did, and in the morning, when he remembered the events of the night before, he laughed and laughed.

"If I can be calm after a night like that," he explained to the puzzled nurse, "I'm safe!"

Before long he was allowed visitors. One of the first was Stim.

"You certainly gave us a scare, old man," he said.

"But I made it, thanks to the moon," replied Dr. Goddard.

Stim wondered whether his friend was delirious again.

"Thanks to the *moon?*" he asked.

"Why, sure," laughed Dr. Goddard. "The position of the moon determines the date of Easter, and if Easter vacation hadn't come early, well . . ."

"Dear old moon," said Stim.

Now, for the second time in his life, Dr. Goddard was faced with a slow recovery from long illness. But this time he had the consolation of knowing that the space dream was far enough along so that he could get right on with it as soon as he was well.

The following October 19 he walked shakily to the old cherry tree where exactly fourteen years before he had first had the vision of a gleaming space projectile. Ever since that day, he had tried to keep this anniversary. Whether he could visit the tree or not, he would use the day to sum up the year past, and plan for the one ahead. Especially when he could actually lean against the ancient trunk, the experience seemed to refresh him and give him new determination.

On this particular anniversary he decided that the time had come to get some of his ideas patented in Washington. He knew that a scientist's work could slip out of his hands without this protection. (Thanks to patent coverage, fifteen years after Dr. Goddard's death his widow and his financial backers, the Daniel and Florence Guggenheim Foundation, were granted a million dollars by the government. This was in recognition of the use that the Air Force, the Army, the Space Agency and the Navy had all made of the ideas described in his patents.)

In the summer of 1914, he was granted the two patents which best describe what the "Goddard Rocket" is. The claims of these patents cover three broad principles. The first is the use of a combustion chamber with a nozzle to allow the escape of gas from the chamber. The second is the system of feeding solid or liquid fuel into this chamber, to give either steady or intermittent propulsive force. The third principle describes the use of multistage rockets, each stage being dropped off as the propellant it contains is used up.

By the fall of this year Dr. Goddard was able to teach at Clark University, part-time. And he was planning on actually shooting rockets within a few months. Though they were hardly the elaborate, liquid-propelled devices described in his patents and notebooks, they would be a start. He had bought some ships' rockets, originally meant for sending up signals, and he had worked out some improvements.

It was a great day when one of these little rockets soared across a small pond at the height of nearly five hundred feet. Afterward, back he went to the laboratory, to work on steel combustion chambers and nozzles and the vacuum experiments, which would take the rocket out of the firecracker class.

Stim sometimes marveled that his friend could carry on conscientiously with his teaching when his heart was really with the rocket work.

"Doesn't all that lecturing bother you?" he asked, after Dr. Goddard had had a particularly hard week.

Dr. Goddard laughed. "That reminds me of a story," he

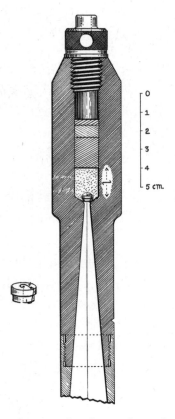

1915 diagram of combustion chamber and nozzle of dry-fuel rocket

said in his best speechmaking manner. "It took place in a small prohibition town in the West. A train stopped at the station, and a man put his head out the window, calling to the bystanders that a woman had just fainted. Did anyone have any whisky? A man on the platform reluctantly produced a flask from his pocket, about half full. The man at the window raised it to his lips and drained it to the last drop. As the train pulled out he said to the astonished specta-

tors, 'It always did make me nervous to see a woman faint!'
Now, it always did make *me* nervous to give a speech, but *I*
have to make the best of it!"

So Dr. Goddard did make the best of his teaching duties,
and treasured the time he could give to the rocket. In this
way life went quite smoothly. His only concern was for
Gram, who had become very feeble. She died in the fall of
1916 within a few days of Dr. Goddard's traditional walk
to the cherry tree. That year there was a lot to remember
when he visited the tree for the yearly summing up. And
a great sadness when he thought that she would now never
see the triumph of the rocket dream, which had been almost
as much a part of her as it was of him.

Leading a pleasantly isolated life, dividing his time between teaching and experimenting, Dr. Goddard found it
hard to believe that for two years a bitter war had been going
on on the other side of the Atlantic. How could such a thing
possibly affect a young professor, quietly going about his
business, with a vast ocean between him and the war? But
by the fall of 1916 fifteen nations were involved in the First
World War. It didn't seem likely that the United States
could remain neutral when one by one her natural allies
were swept into the conflict.

Dr. Goddard had recently sent a summary of his work
to the Smithsonian Institution in Washington, asking them
for money to support the development of the rocket. Early
in the winter these funds were granted.

R. H. Goddard with steel combustion chamber and nozzle
for rocket, 1915

"Did you tell them you had weapons in mind when you asked for the money?" asked Stim.

"No, and I didn't have, at the time. But things have happened pretty fast in the past few weeks. The men at the Smithsonian read the newspapers like everyone else, and a look at the headlines these days puts a new light on things."

Five

U-Boat Sinks U.S. Merchantman . . . Fifth U.S. Ship
Downed in North Atlantic! . . .

This was the way the headlines read by early spring, 1917.
Everybody knew that a declaration of war upon Germany
was only a matter of days.

From his laboratory at Clark University, Dr. Goddard
wrote a letter to Dr. Abbot, at the Smithsonian Institution.
He was happy to report that the work was going well. There
were infinite possibilities for the rocket in warfare, it seemed.
It could be used as a weapon to defend our coast, if need be.
Or as a method for long-range bombardment. It might also
be developed as a hand-weapon, a device which the foot
soldier could use against the onslaught of the German tank.
If the Smithsonian would continue to support it, the rocket
could surely do its part in any war effort.

War was declared in April, and within a few months there
would be money to pay for the needed research. Dr. Goddard
commenced the development of weapons under the United

States Signal Corps. This shift from the purely academic life held some interesting surprises, now that he found himself and his invention actually involved in the war.

On a trip to New York to consult with an Army general on rocket matters, Dr. Goddard was startled to have the general give a demonstration of secrecy. He had already assumed that one didn't discuss the latest developments in weapons with just anyone; but the general introduced the young scientist to some of his own friends by saying, "My friend Dr. Goddard is working on some weather forecasting devices."

Fortunately Dr. Goddard could talk convincingly about weather devices until the subject was changed.

"Well," he said to himself on the way home from New York, "if *that's* the way it is, I'd better get a night watchman for the lab."

But he still couldn't quite believe that enemy spies would trouble themselves with the doings of a university professor on a quiet New England campus. His mind was on other things by the time he reached his laboratory.

So he was shocked to find his once peaceful and orderly laboratory in an uproar upon his return. There was evidence that the place had been broken into on at least one occasion while he was gone. And now an important set of calculations was missing.

"He says he dropped the papers on the way home, last night!" explained one of the technicians, referring to a fellow worker. "It was black as your hat, and raining and blowing like anything, and he says the stuff just blew out of his hands. He's out looking for it now."

The possibilities of this situation were alarming. Dr. Goddard shuddered to think that in the twenty-four hours before the papers were recovered, they *might* actually have been on loan to enemy agents. Suddenly he realized how realistic the general's warnings had been. The Goddard rocket *could* be in danger of being turned against our own forces! Something must be done.

He had just finished a telephone call to the chief of police, to arrange a night patrol of the laboratory area, when there was a knock at the door. A little old lady came in, explaining that she was a neighbor from across the street.

"It's not that we mind the noise," she said. "After all, we know that all those explosions must be very useful to the war effort. But I think you should know that it makes your neighbors very uneasy to see people sneaking around and peeking through your laboratory windows at all hours of the night."

No sooner had his visitor left, more or less pacified by Dr. Goddard's promise of police protection for the area, than one of the laboratory workers stormed in to see him.

"Sir," said the young man, "It can't be done. We're all going mad. With that monster down the street snapping and popping in the middle of our tests, we can't get results worth a plug nickel."

Dr. Goddard shook his head in bewilderment. From spies to monsters . . . What next?

" 'Monster,' you say?" he asked.

"Yes!" cried his frustrated assistant. "Every time we start to take a reading on our apparatus that ruddy trolley car lumbers past outside and mixes up the instruments. We don't know half the time if we're measuring the thrust we need to bash in a German tank, or the voltage needed to get from here to Boston by trolley!"

Right then Dr. Goddard decided that a laboratory in the middle of a busy town was not the ideal place for carrying out wartime research. So he was considerably relieved when —thanks to the efforts of the Smithsonian—the Signal Corps offered him the use of its facilities in a wilderness area of California, as well as more money to carry on the weapons research. No nervous neighbors, no trolley cars, and no threat of spies!

A friend came around on the last day before the departure for California, wondering if he could help.

"I suspect you can," said Dr. Goddard, "If you've got a good strong safe in your office." He handed over a fat envelope of papers. "This stuff is to be read only by an optimist," he explained, "because anyone else would say the writer was crazy. But if anything should happen to me before this war is over, you'll know where to find my most recent ideas, for what they're worth. And if the wrong side wins out, just see that they aren't found at all."

"I'll take care of it," his friend assured him. "It sounds as if it might be worth looking after."

Dr. Goddard laughed. "Oh," he said, "most of it you've

heard before: the solar energy business, some ideas about atomic energy, and then the speculation about how to avoid collision with meteors in outer space, once we get there."

He paused, and the other man waited. When he saw that Dr. Goddard hardly knew how to go on, he said quietly, "I've never laughed yet, have I, Bob?"

"All right, all right." Dr. Goddard spoke in a rush, as if he hoped to get a confession over with quickly. "Most of what I've put in that envelope I call 'The Ultimate Migration.' It has to do with what will surely be the last pioneering effort of the human race, and my ideas on how the migration can be accomplished. And do you want to hear how I think it will be done?" He looked at his friend.

"I'm not laughing yet, Bob," was the calm reply.

Dr. Goddard drew a deep breath. "I truly believe," he said, "that it will eventually be possible for human beings to be transported on expeditions to distant stars—leaving earth while they are in a kind of deep sleep the way seeds 'sleep' over the winter, and waking up at their destination as much as a thousand years later!"

There was a moment's stunned silence.

"It's a shocker, Bob. But, knowing you, I'm still not laughing."

Dr. Goddard sealed the envelope. On the outside he wrote, "Formulae for Re-silvering Mirrors."

"There," he said. "That sounds dull enough to discourage anyone from looking inside!"

The transfer of Dr. Goddard's work from Worcester to

California took place in great secrecy. Even the license plate of the car carrying the experimental apparatus from the laboratory to the railroad station was covered with a strip of canvas. Dr. Goddard boarded the train carrying a heavy bag.

"Explosives!" he told the porter who offered to carry his luggage. The porter laughed nervously. Probably just a fellow wanting to avoid a tip to the porter, but you never knew. . . . If the man *had* known the contents of the bag he would have run for miles.

The work went well in California, and by the fall of 1918 Dr. Goddard and his group knew that they had developed a weapon which would give the infantryman a good chance against the enemy's tanks.

A demonstration was arranged to take place at the Army's proving grounds at Aberdeen, Maryland. Men from the Signal Corps, the Army Air Corps, and Army Ordnance waited eagerly to see what Dr. Goddard's group had produced.

General Dunwoody and some other officers were talking while Dr. Goddard and his team set up their apparatus.

"As I understand it," explained the general, "this weapon is really a portable rocket launcher, small enough for a foot soldier to carry. It's a tube in which cartridges are shot into a combustion chamber by small charges of powder."

"In other words," said another officer, "the Roman candle has gone to war! But, good heavens, what is Goddard up to out there? Is the man going to show us a gun or is he planning to conduct a symphony?"

General Dunwoody looked and laughed. "I told you Dr. Goddard was a good Yankee! If it works just as well to prop his rockets on a couple of old music stands instead of buying something fancier, you can bet he'll do it that way!"

The demonstration was successful. The two-inch projectiles traveled straight and fast, penetrating a sandbox and two sandbags at a distance of seven hundred and fifty yards.

"That thing could really wallop a tank," the generals agreed. (And they were right. In a later war the "bazooka" did just that.)

It now looked as if the Army would surely put money into rocket development. But within a few days—on November eleventh, 1918—the Armistice was signed. The Army's interest in rocketry ended, not to be revived for another twenty years. Government funds for weapons were drastically cut. (No one realized it then, but when this happened our country suffered a setback in the "race for space" which is going on today. Dr. Goddard surely could have accomplished a great deal then with a fraction of the funds we are spending on rocket development now. Unfortunately, we lost a fine headstart before the race even began.)

The government's indifference meant that Dr. Goddard had to resume work on the shoestring budget which he could get through occasional grants by the Smithsonian Institution. Again Dr. Goddard had occasion to be grateful to Clark and whatever support Clark University could afford to give.

One stormy evening Dr. Goddard sat with President San-

R. H. Goddard loading the 1918 "bazooka" with three-inch projectile,
Mt. Wilson Observatory, 1918

ford in the older man's library, discussing Dr. Goddard's
plans for the rocket.

"I can tell you one thing, Bob," said President Sanford.
"There's at least one fellow at the University who says if
you don't publish what you've done so far with the rocket.
he will! What are you going to do about that?"

Dr. Goddard remembered his own words to Gram: *"If you
want people to support your research, they've got to understand what you're trying to do. Publish whatever you can
get accepted by a publisher."* Yes, the time had come to as-
semble his results to date, and explain to the world what
his rocket dream was all about.

"You're right, of course, sir," said Dr. Goddard. "But I'll certainly need a supersecretary to make some kind of sense out of all those years of notes! *And* know enough to keep quiet about her work. Oh, yes, *and* not be too awful to look at, if possible."

Meanwhile, not far away, a very determined young lady was arguing with her mother.

"Esther, you simply *may* not go out in this storm at this hour of the night! It can wait till tomorrow."

"No, Mother, it can't. President Sanford is going on a trip tomorrow, and his secretary is leaving to get married. The university might find him a new girl while he's away, and *I* want the job!" The door closed behind her.

Sometime later the doorbell rang at President Sanford's house. He opened the door, and in came one of the wettest young creatures he or Dr. Goddard had ever seen.

Esther Kisk refused to come beyond the front hall.

"I'm pretty wet!" she apologized. This was an understatement. Water streamed from her normally tidy blond hair; puddles formed around her feet as she stood there dripping.

"My name is Esther Kisk," she panted, "and I just came to say that if you haven't found a secretary yet, I'd like to have the job. I've worked as a clerk for a year, and I want to go on to college sometime. Can I have the job? I've been to night school for typing and shorthand." While she stopped for breath Dr. Sanford made up his mind.

"Miss Kisk," he said gravely, "I will look forward to seeing

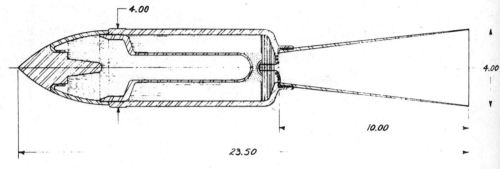

Preliminary design for four-inch aircraft projectile, 1918

you at work in my office three weeks from now. Just don't get washed away in the meantime!"

She was gone in an instant, refusing the men's offer to take her home.

The older man took up the conversation where they had left off.

"You might get the Smithsonian to publish your paper when it's finished," he said. "That wouldn't be bad."

Dr. Goddard stretched his long legs toward the fire, and pyramided his finger tips. "Not bad at all," he mused. "Once she dries out, not bad at all, I bet. And smart!"

President Sanford chuckled. "The lady has just become *my* secretary, Goddard," he said. "But her evenings are her own. She looks to me like one who could probably cope with the Goddard rocket in her spare time."

In the course of the next few weeks Dr. Goddard found a remarkable number of reasons for turning up at President Sanford's office. And he somehow always seemed to arrive when the president wasn't there, but Miss Kisk was! Then, when she agreed to do some of his typing in her spare time, the work on his manuscript made an excellent excuse for frequent visits to her family's house.

Dr. Goddard would arrive on week ends and evenings, armed with the tidy blue folders which were practically his trade mark.

"You can't judge a book by its cover, they say, but I'm not taking any chances," he insisted.

Another pet theory was that only he could punch the holes in the manuscript pages properly. While he dictated, and Miss Kisk typed, he would pace up and down the living room—punching away, shedding little white dots as he went.

One evening, as he was leaving, he whispered that he was beginning to wonder if Miss Kisk's mother had taken a dislike to him.

"She watches my every move while I'm here," he said, "and she doesn't seem to like what she sees!"

Esther Kisk laughed. "You just don't know how Mother feels about housekeeping. Look at the living room floor!"

The otherwise spotless carpet was covered with a small snowdrift of tiny white dots. After that evening, Dr. Goddard left his beloved punch at home. He had no wish to offend the lady whom he hoped might one day be his mother-in-law.

But progress with his courtship was pretty slow for some time. When he first asked Miss Kisk for a date her reaction was a firm "Certainly not." But he was patient and persistent, reasoning philosophically that a man in his thirties probably seemed incredibly ancient to a girl in her teens.

After a while the refusals gradually gave way to an occasional "Yes," and before long the difference in their ages might not have existed. One day, to her own surprise, Esther Kisk realized that it didn't matter at all.

Meanwhile, work on the preparation of the paper continued. It took the better part of a year to finish it; but finally, late in 1919, *A Method of Reaching Extreme Altitudes* was published by the Smithsonian Institution.

It was a historic event. This paper was to become a classic in the literature of rocket and jet propulsion, since it laid the foundation for nearly all of today's developments in rocketry. But its first public appearance was practically a catastrophe.

Dr. Goddard waited anxiously to find how the public would feel about the work he had done. If they liked his ideas there might be more money forthcoming from the Smithsonian so that he could go further.

For a time, strangely, there seemed to be no interest in the book at all. Then all at once there was far more clamor than he would have wished.

It seemed that he had added to his factual report some of his favorite ideas on the eventual possibilities of space flight. (The space dream had been irrepressible.) Among other things, he had suggested the possibility of propelling a charge of flash powder to the dark side of the moon, so that its surface could be observed through a strong telescope.

These were purely speculative remarks. But a press representative from the Institution, who must have been a frustrated space traveler, made much of them — ignoring the sound work in the main body of the paper. As a result, the newspapers gleefully seized upon Dr. Goddard's work as "moon rocket" research.

One reporter wrote in a New York paper that the inventor "didn't even know high school physics." This was a remarkable comment to make about a man who had long since received his doctor's degree in the subject, and was now head of the Physics Department of an important university.

The remarks were ridiculous, but they hurt nevertheless.

"From now on I'll keep that kind of thing locked away, like the 'Formulae for Re-silvering Mirrors,'" he told Esther Kisk in disgust.

But he couldn't get the newspapers' distortion of his remarks off his mind. The world had learned prematurely and incompletely about some of his most cherished ideas. Very well, if the sensational idea of "moon shooting" had caught the public fancy, let them read his answers to some of the criticism that "cried down" his theories! The *Tech Alumni Bulletin* published these answers in 1920.

One of the things that people with half-knowledge could not understand was the old question of how a rocket could progress in the vacuum of outer space. What could it push against if there was "nothing" behind it to be pushed? Dr. Goddard asked his readers to think of the gas ejected from a rocket nozzle as a charge of fine shot from a gun, moving very fast. The chamber would "kick" as this charge was fired, exactly as a gun kicks. It would be this "kick" forward, rather than the discharge of gases backward, that would propel the rocket. So what did the nothingness of outer space matter?

Others protested that a rocket would never reach this vacuum in the first place. After all, they said, a body moving through the atmosphere at speeds up to one and a half miles per second would certainly catch fire, or disintegrate. It would fail to withstand the friction caused by tearing through masses of air molecules at such speeds.

Not necessarily, said Dr. Goddard, and he reminded his readers that the earth travels through space at ten times this speed. "But," he pointed out, "this does not cause anyone any noticeable inconvenience."

Concerning hitting the moon, it had been argued that in the vastness of outer space it would be impossible to direct a rocket to the right spot. Dr. Goddard suggested the photo-electric cell as a means of guiding a rocket towards a shining object, such as the moon. (Today we've all seen the door of a supermarket swing open as if by magic as we approach. In this case we have cut *off* the light from a lamp beamed at such a cell. So the door goes "off course"—and opens.)

Once this article was published, Dr. Goddard felt he had done all he could for the time being to defend the much-maligned rocket dream. If the public understood a little more about his theories now, so much the better. But in any case, he would get on with the work.

By 1920 he was working entirely with liquid propellants for the rocket motors he was testing in the laboratory at

Clark. Solid fuels had been satisfactory for fairly short, horizontal flights, such as had been made in the testing of the
"bazooka" type of device. But for the purpose of lifting a
larger rocket, and keeping it vertical, these fuels were too
temperamental: if packed a little too tightly they burned too
slowly, and the rocket wouldn't lift at all in its test frame;
too loosely packed, they merely caused a sudden, useless
explosion.

So Dr. Goddard began the important job of working out
the necessary rocket "plumbing" to pump liquid oxygen and
a liquid fuel, such as gasoline, from separate tanks into the
combustion chamber. In the combustion chamber the two
liquids combined and burned, and with this burning they
turned to very hot gases under great pressure. The tremendous force of this expansion lifted the rocket. It was the
beginning of a never-ending task, a constant devising of new
ways to "feed" his rockets as they became more complicated
and demanding.

This complicated engineering meant buying new apparatus for the laboratory, and unfortunately funds from the
Smithsonian were at a low ebb. But Clark University helped
out, and, as always, Dr. Goddard shopped for materials like
a good Yankee trader. It was a fine thing when he found a
chemical firm nearby which whenever it emptied its vats
threw away liquid oxygen. He could have it, when available,
for a dollar a liter, if he would come to get it before it was
tossed out.

This meant he must have a car. Soon Dr. Goddard was the

proud part owner, with some friends, of an almost new Chevrolet. But alas, when he started to drive it away from the show room, there was a rumble and a clank and the rear axle parted company from the chassis!

"I must have jostled it when I signed the check for the salesman," he told Esther Kisk gloomily.

The next adventure in car owning was with an Oakland.

"Now *there's* a real car!" he said confidently. And for a while all went well. He built a pair of racks on the running boards, in which he carried the great bottles of liquid oxygen.

This caused his friends some concern.

"Don't drop an axle while you're driving *this* one," urged Dr. Roope, a former graduate student of Dr. Goddard's. "The lab's the place to mix oxygen and gasoline, not the highway."

He spoke with special feeling. *His* car was to lead the way to a faculty outing the next day, with Dr. Goddard following in the Oakland. Dr. Goddard assured his young friend that of course the precious bottles would not be on board.

On the day of the picnic the two cars got into a traffic snarl on the way out of town, and by the time Dr. Roope made his way through it the Oakland was nowhere in sight. He drove along slowly, waiting for his friend to catch up, and in a few minutes the other car appeared, limping along at a snail's pace. Watching its erratic progress in his rear-view mirror, Dr. Roope was horrified to see that there was no sign of the driver. He pulled to the side of the road and ran back, in time to see Dr. Goddard pop up behind the wheel, then disappear an instant later. Jumping on the running board, Dr. Roope looked into the car and discovered his friend down on the floor, frantically shifting gears with the stub of the floor-mounted gear-shift. It had broken clean off in the middle of the traffic jam.

"She goes just fine," panted Dr. Goddard, "but I sure could use a navigator."

Dr. Roope climbed in and "navigated" to the side of the road.

"Tell me, Bob, what do you think of this Oakland?"

Dr. Goddard sighed. "Percy," he said, "do you see that billboard over there?" He pointed to a cigarette advertisement.

Dr. Roope looked, and burst out laughing.

The sign read: I'VE TRIED THEM ALL. GIVE ME A CAMEL!

"That sums it up," said Dr. Goddard.

Six

The next two years were lonely for Dr. Goddard. Esther Kisk was away at college, leading her class and writing back glowing accounts of college life. She sounded very gay, he thought, and he worried a little when he heard about the good times she was having. He told himself that this was selfish and unreasonable, but it didn't seem to make him feel any better. "Why did she have to choose a co-educational college?" he asked himself grumpily.

But at least there was plenty of work to keep him busy. There was his teaching at Clark as well as the constant pressure from the Smithsonian Institution to get on with the rocket. They were naturally anxious to see what their money was going to produce. Laboratory experiments were all very fine, but when would a liquid-fueled rocket fly?

At the same time he was surprised to find that not only his patrons were watching him closely. In 1922 a letter came from Professor Hermann Oberth, of Rumania, saying that he, too, was interested in a method of "passing over the earth's atmosphere." He asked for all the books and papers that the American inventor had published on the subject, and Dr. Goddard sent him a copy of the Smithsonian's 1919 paper on his work, "A Method of Reaching Extreme Altitudes." There didn't seem to be any good reason not to, since anyone who really wanted to read it could secure a copy free from the Smithsonian, anyway.

Professor Oberth later was active in the German Interplanetary Society which was drafted by Hitler for military work in World War II. The V-2 missile which Germany produced at this time was almost identical with the Goddard rocket as described in this early publication.

The Japanese, Italian and other embassies also asked for information. In fact, the essence of rocketry was available through the Smithsonian Institution to whoever was interested.

But Dr. Goddard didn't consider anything sinister in this world-wide interest. The aim was to get on with the work, so that the rocket could start gathering information about the universe beyond the earth. If an exchange of ideas with other scientists could further this dream, so much the better.

Before long there was a valuable addition to the rocket group at Clark. After her sophomore year, Esther Kisk's savings were gone, and she returned to her job at Clark in order to be able to finish college later. Thanks to Dr. Goddard's powers of persuasion she was soon saving for a wedding trousseau instead!

Some of Dr. Goddard's own savings now went into a

"Sept" motion-picture camera—so-called, he maintained, because it could be counted on to run for seven seconds at the most.

Young Mrs. Goddard attended all the rocket tests as official photographer, even though "Sept" was likely to run down before the rocket lifted in the frame.

"She cooks pretty well, too," said Dr. Goddard proudly, when Dr. Roope admired the bride's photography.

"And a good thing," replied his friend. "You were a lean and hungry bachelor for too long!"

The rocket was thriving, too; in December, 1925, a twelve-pound rocket lifted in the testing frame for twenty-seven seconds. It was the first liquid-propelled rocket ever to lift its

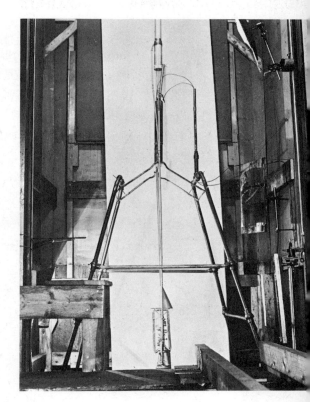

Rocket in testing frame, Clark
University, August 1925

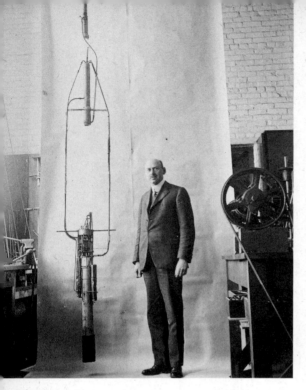

Complete rocket with double-acting engine, November 1925

own weight, and operated in very much the way Dr. Goddard had predicted in his patent, eleven years before.

"There'll be no holding her now," he told Mrs. Goddard. "We'll have to give her room!"

The roomiest place he could think of was the farm of an old friend of the family a few miles out of town.

"Of course you can shoot your rocket out here, Robert," said "Aunt". Effie. "There'll be no one to bother you." Since anything her "nephew" Robert did was all right with her, it never occurred to her that the rocket might cause some bother.

But certainly for a while there was remarkably little commotion at the launching site.

Watching the activity from the farmhouse, her real nephew said to Aunt Effie, "It's a funny thing, but Bob's rocket doesn't seem to *do* much! He keeps hauling the thing out here and firing it off, and all that happens is that something sticks and it goes over on its nose! I mean, isn't it supposed to *fly*?"

"Rome wasn't built in a day, Asa!" snapped his aunt. "As a matter of fact, Robert told me this morning he'll be glad if the rocket clears the tower."

So again and again, whenever Dr. Goddard could spare time from his teaching, the rocket made the trip from the laboratory at Clark to the farm in Auburn. On the worst winter days its frail frame was tenderly transported in a horse-drawn sleigh. Considering his past experiences with the liquid-fueled automobile, it wasn't surprising that in bad driving weather he preferred to entrust the rocket to the reliable, solid-fuel hay-burner!

As Asa said, the rocket was no beauty. It was a spindly, skeletal device, ten feet long, and on top it had a combustion chamber about the size of a Fourth of July rocket. The propellant tanks were slung below. Two spindly pipes ran from the tanks up to the chamber.

"Quaint," was Mrs. Goddard's word for it, but she added loyally that the Wright brothers' plane hadn't been much to look at, either.

In the morning of March 16, 1926, the rocket and its attendants set out from the university once again. It traveled by car this time, and with it were Dr. and Mrs. God-

Rocket and fixtures in horse-drawn sled, winter 1926–1927

dard, Dr. Roope, and Dr. Goddard's assistant, Henry Sachs. The launching stand was towed behind on a trailer.

It was an unusually clear morning, crisp and cold. There was only the sound of metal parts being assembled, and the cranking noise of "Sept" being readied for action.

By early afternoon everything was in order. Henry Sachs lighted the primitive motor with a blowtorch on the end of a long pole. Then Dr. Goddard pulled the release cable which anchored the rocket. For a few breathless seconds, which seemed like minutes, absolutely nothing happened. In these moments the rocket did not lift, but there was a flame

Testing frame and windbreak at Ward farm, Auburn, Mass., March 1926

and a steady roar. Then the rocket began to rise, like a reluctant beast from a long sleep. Gaining speed, it tore upward till it cleared the frame. Faster and faster it went. Only when it had reached four times its own height, and a speed of sixty miles an hour, did the rocket begin to lose altitude. Then it curved off to the left, smashing up in a muddy cabbagefield two hundred and twenty feet away.

Dr. Goddard standing beside the framework holding the first liquid-propellant rocket to give a flight (March 16, 1926, at Auburn, Mass.)

The crew picked up every scrap of the crumpled rocket and the scattered bits and pieces. Everything that could be salvaged would be used again.

Looking at the wreckage, Dr. Goddard realized that one of the problems he would eventually have to solve would be how to ease the rocket's landing. The delicate instruments he planned to send up wouldn't be very useful if they ended in a thousand pieces!

This was the flight that led off the great procession across the skies of all the V-2s and the Redstones and the Atlases, and their successors, that were to follow. As a first attempt it compares favorably with the Wright brothers' much-publicized first flight, in 1902, which had traveled a little more than half the distance, at a quarter the height.

On the ride home Mrs. Goddard was very quiet.

"What's the trouble?" her husband asked. "We've just made history, and you look as if you'd lost your last friend."

"There wasn't anybody but *us* to see our flight," complained Mrs. Goddard.

"Now there's a woman's vanity for you," said her husband. "After all, *we* saw it happen, and the rest of the world will see it when you develop the films from 'Sept.' "

"That's just it!" she wailed. " 'Sept' ran down just as the rocket woke up!" The photographer was completely disgusted.

The Smithsonian Institution was not terribly impressed by Dr. Goddard's written report of the first successful flight of a liquid-propelled rocket. They wanted something bigger, better, and faster—and soon.

Parts of first liquid-propellant rocket after flight, March 16, 1926, with
Henry Sachs, Dr. Goddard, Dr. Roope

"If you want to keep people happy, do it yesterday!" he
said to himself when he heard this reaction.

There was another flight on April third, and then, because
of the Institution's insistence, work began on trying to make
a much bigger rocket perform as well as the smaller ones
had. These "big sitters," as Mrs. Goddard called the great
reluctant machines, were twenty times larger than the 1926
model.

There was no flight of the monster rocket during this
period, nor for many years to come, but nevertheless new
things were being learned all the while; and, one by one,
problems were being solved.

One of these had been the effect on metal of the intense cold of liquid oxygen, about minus 300 degrees Fahrenheit. It caused every metal Dr. Goddard used to become brittle. Then, when suddenly exposed to the tremendous heat of combustion, the chamber burned through again and again.

He solved this problem for the time being when he used sheet-steel to make the combustion chamber. When the motor became even more powerful, he knew he would have to find something else, but for now, it worked.

By 1928 it was clear that in attempting unsuccessfully to fly the big rocket, invention was being pushed beyond reasonable limits. In December, with the rocket reduced to just four times its 1926 weight of six pounds empty, there was a successful flight.

In July, 1929, Dr. Goddard towed his most elaborate rocket so far out to the farm at Auburn. It was one of the first instrument-carrying rockets, being equipped with a barometer, thermometer, and a small camera placed in such a way as to record the instrument readings at the highest point of flight, in case there should be another flight at last. The camera was designed to be started automatically by the jerking of a parachute which would be ejected at the moment the rocket began to lose altitude.

There was a successful launching, and a good flight, lasting eighteen and a half seconds. The rocket rose ninety feet and traveled horizontally one hundred and seventy-one feet.

Two members had joined the same team which had

Rocket in tower ready for test, July 17, 1929

Beginning of rocket flight, July 17, 1929

Continuation of rocket flight, July 17, 1929

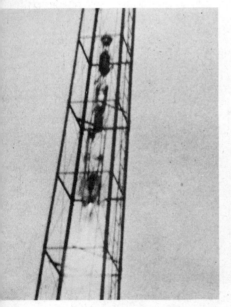

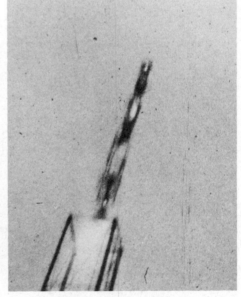

Rocket nearing top of 60-foot tower, July 17, 1929

Rocket in flight July 17, 1929

launched the rocket in 1926, so that six were on hand to
pick up the remains when once again it dashed itself to bits
on its return to earth.

As they were gathering up the last re-usable scraps, they
heard the sound of an airplane motor. In a minute a small
biplane came in sight, circled the farm several times and
bustled off.

"Too bad," said Dr. Goddard. "He just missed the show."

They were about ready to leave when Mrs. Goddard
pointed to a cloud of dust on the road.

"It looks like another latecomer," said Dr. Roope.

Rocket after landing, July 17, 1929 (*Left to right:* L. Mansur, R. H.
Goddard, H. Sachs, A. Kisk, P. Roope)

This was an understatement. Within minutes the six rocket workers were surrounded by police cars, an ambulance, and several cars marked "Press."

"Stand back, everyone!" bellowed a police officer. "Make room for the doctor!"

A young intern pushed his way through the crowd, clutching his black bag.

Meanwhile, an enterprising reporter had cornered Henry Sachs, Dr. Goddard's assistant.

"I only want a brief statement, Mr. Sachs," he said briskly. "Just the names and addresses of the victims of the plane crash."

"But I keep trying to tell you," cried Sachs, "there *was no airplane,* and it didn't crash! That is, there was an airplane, but it came around after the rocket landed, and then it went away."

The reporter's eye lighted up. "Rockets, eh?" he said. "Well, there's a story here all right! . . . Great Scott, just look at the rocks!"

The rocks he referred to were a pile of large stones arranged at the base of the launching tower so that the blast from the rocket nozzle wouldn't raise a screen of dust and obscure the view of the rocket's lifting.

"That rocket motor must be getting pretty powerful," he marveled. "You've got nothing left but burnt pebbles from this test. I sure can see why you've put the fuel tanks on top, instead of underneath the way you had them at the beginning. What a flame like that couldn't do to a tankful of gasoline!" He hustled off, not too sorry to have missed an actual test.

The police chief, meanwhile, finding no "victims" for the young intern to minister to, had finally been convinced that there had been no airplane crash.

Someone had seen the rocket in flight, it seemed, and mistaking it for an airplane crashing in flames had called the police. The little biplane had been sent over to look for the wreckage.

Dr. Goddard patiently explained what had really happened, and what he was trying to do, and asked the newsmen not to make a sensation of it in the papers. But by the time he and Mrs. Goddard reached home, some weary hours later, extra editions were already coming out featuring the explosion in midair of a rocket to the moon.

Horrified, he gave another statement to the press. There had been no attempt at anything as spectacular as a flight to the moon, he protested. And although a rocket was a noisy thing, there had been no explosion in mid-air, and no harm to anything except the rocket itself upon landing. The Smithsonian Institution backed him up, explaining that the inventor was merely looking for ways of getting weather information at high altitudes.

But the damage was done. Professor Goddard was declared a menace, and state officials called upon him to tell him that no more rocket experiments might be held in Massachusetts.

The day when this news was printed a graduate student

who had been present at the test stormed into his professor's laboratory waving the newspaper.

"They ain't done right by our Nell!" he cried.

Poor "Nell," as she was ever after known, was starting out in life with a sorry reputation.

Luckily there was more than one person who sympathized with the embarrassed inventor when he read the strange accounts of Nell's first flight. Reading between the lines, Colonel Charles Lindbergh guessed that this man Goddard was really quite like himself, dedicated to the idea of mechanical flight. Lindbergh had made his famous crossing of the Atlantic two years before, in a tiny plane called *The Spirit of St. Louis*. Probably people had thought *him* a little mad to make even the attempt.

Certainly no one knew better than he how many problems there were in making and operating a flying machine. And as for long vertical flights without the control of a pilot! ... The flyer felt that anyone who had made a good start on such a project deserved help.

He made a surprise telephone call to the house on Maple Hill, and shyly asked if the professor would be willing to see him.

"I think some friends of mine could help Dr. Goddard," he explained.

Nell certainly needed help if she was ever to fly again. Not only was she homeless for the time being, but she was almost penniless as well.

Dr. Goddard and Colonel Lindbergh talked for a long

time about the rocket and her problems, and the flyer offered
to find new financial backing for further work. He would
talk first to the duPont family, and proposed that Dr. Goddard fly down to Wilmington, Delaware, with him in his
two-seater plane.

"On the way you can get a good look at this big, blue sky
you want to conquer," he said.

It was an unnerving trip.

"What's the matter, professor?" asked the pilot as he
brought the little plane out of a particularly steep dive.
"You're the man who's going to launch the space age!"

Dr. Goddard looked a little green.

"I'm beginning to agree with some of those newspaper
people who suggest I ought to come down to earth. It's both
feet on the ground for me, from now on. Hey, watch out for
those trees, will you?" he cried as a giant stand of pines
swung giddily past the cockpit.

"Wonderful scenery around here," replied Lindbergh
calmly as he took the plane back "upstairs" again. "There,"
he said. "That's the kind of place you'll need for the rocket
station. Plenty of good, flat acreage."

"And plenty expensive, too, I'm afraid," replied Dr. Goddard.

"Well, money is what we're out to get," said his friend
cheerfully. "Now, hold on to your hat. I'm going down for
another look at the scenery."

In its sudden descent from five thousand to fifty feet, the
little plane coughed, but quickly recovered. Dr. Goddard

spent much of the last part of the trip with his eyes tightly closed.

During their visit to the duPonts, Dr. Goddard was strangely quiet. There was no question that the family was interested in the rocket and its commercial possibilities; but somehow, as their engineers became more and more enthusiastic, the inventor grew increasingly uneasy.

He pictured a tremendous industrial organization producing a long line of commercial rockets. He could imagine the business being so successful that no one would care about the wonderful things the rocket might do if she were allowed to go on growing.

"Why, she'd be absolutely stifled!" he thought to himself.

It wasn't easy to translate basic research into terms that could be understood by the people who had the dollars to support it. It was hard to explain what might be gained by the sending of one noisy machine a little farther from the earth than had been reached by the one before it. The possibility of being able to record temperatures, wind velocity, and air pressure by sending recording instruments far beyond the earth's surface, and eventually beyond its atmosphere, probably sounded so unlikely that it seemed of doubtful value.

"I just can't see myself in charge of a great mass production of rockets," Dr. Goddard explained to Colonel Lindbergh afterward.

"That's the way it sounded to me, too," agreed his friend. "But never mind. Carry on with Nell as best you can, and I'll let you know as soon as I find someone to back her."

This was in the fall of 1929. While waiting for news from their new friend, Dr. Goddard arranged with the help of Dr. Abbot of the Smithsonian Institution to continue testing Nell in Massachusetts, despite the strong suggestion that she was no longer welcome in that state. The Army said that he could have an unused artillery range at Fort Devens for the time being. The range was in Massachusetts but, being part of an Army base, it was federal not state land.

"And you can't do much damage there that hasn't already been done, in any case," an officer assured Dr. Goddard.

On their first visit to Devens, the Goddards saw right away what he meant. The ex-artillery range was a dismal sight indeed. The skeleton of an old farmhouse dominated the scene, battered and charred by many a barrage of shells. The range itself was a sea of mud.

"But look," said Mrs. Goddard brightly, "there's a little lake. Probably it's quite pretty in the spring."

The "lake" was a good-sized shell crater, filled now with the stagnant water of many rainfalls and melted snows. It was known, appropriately, as "Hell Pond," and whether or not it could be transformed by the coming of spring Dr. Goddard didn't know. He only hoped they would all be far away by then.

No one would have cared how grim her surroundings might be if only Nell could fly. But in order to get her to the range it was necessary to bridge her path across the muddy terrain by improvising a roadbed of fallen trees. Though time and again she left the university laboratory in fine work-

ing order, the twenty-five mile trip from Worcester, plus this
last rugged stretch, did her no good at all. Thus no flights
were attempted during that dreary winter of 1929 to 1930.

During the bitterly cold winter months the rocket team
took shelter between tests in an old henhouse overlooking
Hell Pond. Here they set up a little potbellied stove, salvaged
from the remains of the bombed-out farmhouse. Different
members of the team vied with one another to see who could
produce the tastiest one-dish concoction from various combinations of canned soups, for the midday meal. It was a
great occasion whenever Mrs. Goddard made her way through
the muck, bearing a casserole of real food! The rocket workers became quite attached to their little haven in the henhouse, and it was often hard to go back to work in the biting
cold outside.

But all of them were pleased with Nell. Flights or no
flights, it was evident that she was getting stronger. And they
knew that Lindbergh had not forgotten her; that one day she
would fly again, farther and faster than before.

But meanwhile it was an uneasy winter for the Goddards.

One evening in December Dr. Goddard was listening to a
sports program on the radio while his wife worked in the
kitchen. Suddenly he appeared at her side, chuckling.

"Babe Ruth has the answer," he said. " 'When in a slump,
relax! If you try to get out it lasts longer.' " Much cheered
up, he went back to his radio to hear what else the "Sultan
of Swat" had to say.

"Well," thought Mrs. Goddard, "that's all very well for

the Babe, but the Goddards have a rocket to launch, and I'd like to see him do *that* by relaxing!" She whisked the remains of supper into the icebox, and then began to spread out maps and geodetic surveys on the dining room table.

Gone were the days when they could put aside the business of rocketry and research at the end of the day. Mrs. Goddard thought wistfully of their last trip to a show, when Dr. Goddard had come home happily warbling one of the hit tunes. He had sat at the piano for hours afterward, playing the music by ear.

But there would be time enough for all that later. Now, every night after dinner out came the rainfall charts, the surveys, the maps of every area of the United States which might do for Nell's next home. One after another was ruled out because of too heavy rainfall, generally poor climate, or the type of terrain which might cause unpredictable updrafts.

The professor of meteorology at Clark, Professor Brooks, had heard of their problem and become so interested that he was personally seeing to it that they made no mistake. It was a comforting thing to be part of the academic world, where a man in one specialty was willing to give his time freely and enthusiastically to help a colleague in another branch of scientific work.

While the men discussed the problem, day after day, Mrs. Goddard simply wondered where they would be a year from now. Whatever location suited the rocket, would suit her too.

One evening Dr. Goddard put aside his maps.

"We've got it!" he said. Reading from his notes he quoted,

" 'Average temperature 52.7°, precipitation 14.41 inches. Flat, dry, plains.' "

His wife was relieved. It sounded nice—much better than New England in winter.

"New Mexico is the answer for Nell," continued Dr. Goddard. "All we need now is someone to put us in business."

A few nights later he was writing in his diary. This was always the last task of the day, a ritual which he performed standing at his bureau in his pajamas.

"Just what did Mrs. G. do at Devens today that I should put down here?" he asked his wife.

"I'm afraid she didn't do much except pace the floor of the henhouse and wonder if the phone was ringing at home!" replied Mrs. Goddard. It always amused her that on days when she was actually helping with the tests she was "Mrs. G." in the diary. At other times, she was "E."

"You'd better just say that E. made soup and worried!" she laughed. "And by the way, I *did* somehow feel sure that we'd hear good news from Colonel Lindbergh today. Funny," she yawned.

At that moment the phone rang, and Dr. Goddard dropped the diary and raced for the stairs.

Mrs. Goddard was right behind him, and heard him gasp into the phone, "Twenty-five thousand dollars?"

She quickly pushed a chair under him, and stood by straining her ears to hear what was going on.

She could hear Colonel Lindbergh explaining that he had just shown her films of the launching of Nell to Daniel Guggenheim. This very wealthy man, she knew, was then the president of a foundation whose purpose was to promote "the well-being of mankind."

With all the demands for money that must have fitted into this category, it was lucky for the Goddards that Mr. Guggenheim was far-seeing enough to grasp the possibilities in rockets.

The Daniel Guggenheim Foundation for the promotion of Aeronautics had already established several Schools of Aeronautics.

Now, having heard Lindbergh's description of the rocket project, and seen Mrs. Goddard's films, Daniel Guggenheim wanted to support this new work with his personal grant of twenty-five thousand dollars.

He offered Dr. Goddard this sum for each of two years of research. Another two-year grant totaling fifty thousand dollars was to come when his advisory committee had evaluated what had been accomplished during this period.

Bursting with the good news, Dr. Goddard began to plunge through the pile of correspondence on his desk.

"Where's that map of New Mexico?" he demanded, tossing letters left and right.

Seven

"I just wish your *Traveling in 1950* predictions would come true right now!" sighed Mrs. Goddard. But it wasn't 1950. It was only the early summer of 1930, and the automobile trip diagonally across the country, from Worcester to Roswell, New Mexico, was long and hot. The Goddards had started ahead to look for a place to live, and the four other rocket workers and their wives were to follow.

As the summer scenery changed from the heavy green foliage of New England to the gold of the Great Plains, and then gradually to the reds and purples of the southwest, the sun rose higher and hotter every day. The roads were none too good, and sometimes the Goddards thought enviously of the rocket, which was traveling luxuriously by rail.

Nell and all her paraphernalia had a freight car to themselves, cushioned and supported by every piece of the Goddards' furniture that could be wedged in.

On the last day of the trip, after a long stretch of New Mexico scenery with no sign of a human being, they drove past what seemed to be a filling station with one or two out-buildings. A sign reading High Lonesome flapped in the dry wind.

"What a wonderful name for a gas station," said Mrs. Goddard. "It certainly is high and lonesome, all right." She was beginning to see what people meant when they spoke of the wide open spaces of the West.

On arriving in Roswell, they took a room at the hotel, then immediately went house hunting. Shortly afterward a man from the Roswell Chamber of Commerce introduced them to a real estate agent, a Mr. Turner.

"Oh yes, Dr. Goddard," he said. "I have just what you want. I've talked to the owner of the Eden Valley property, and he says you can set up your experiments any time. And about three miles from here there's a big old ranch house which should make ideal living quarters for you and your people."

The Goddards were flabbergasted. They were still smarting from the reception of Nell back East, and could hardly believe she was being so readily accepted by total strangers.

"I suppose the people at Eden Valley have some idea of what we plan to do, and all," said Dr. Goddard doubtfully.

Mr. Turner was unconcerned. "There are no people at Eden Valley," he said. "Anyway what you do doesn't seem to bother anyone around here much."

When he saw his visitors' amazed and relieved expressions, Mr. Turner smiled.

"That's not so surprising, when you come to think of it.

After all, the grandparents of most of these people came here from the East themselves, not so long ago, looking for plenty of elbow room just as you're doing, if for different reasons. Come to think of it, I guess you could call them space pioneers of a sort.

"All they care about is that you obey the law of the range."

He saw the Goddards looking puzzled again.

"Say," he laughed, "you *are* green, all right! The law of the range simply means that when you go through a gate around here, you leave it open or shut—however you found it. Just start mixing up these herds of cattle, and you may find your neighbors not so neighborly! Otherwise, what you choose to do is your business."

That evening, driving out to their new home, the Mescalero Ranch, Mrs. Goddard yawned a tremendous, happy yawn.

"Open minds are bred by open spaces," she philosophized drowsily, and fell fast asleep.

The next few days were very busy. In the mornings, when

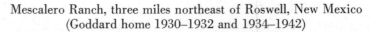

Mescalero Ranch, three miles northeast of Roswell, New Mexico
(Goddard home 1930–1932 and 1934–1942)

Dr. Goddard went off to town to arrange for building a laboratory, his wife worked at getting the ranch house ready for the four families who were to join them.

One exceptionally hot morning, when her husband had gone to superintend the erection of the shop, she decided that a second cup of coffee sipped peacefully in the shade of the terrace would be just the thing to start the day.

Balancing her cup in one hand, she threw open the glass doors to the outside. Then, happening to glance down at her feet, she found herself looking into a pair of cold, beady eyes. A mother tarantula had chosen this cozy spot, between the glass and the screen door, to raise the brood of hairy babies who swarmed about her.

Clutching her coffee cup firmly, Mrs. Goddard said to herself, "I will not, I will *not* be—*Eastern* about this!" Out loud, she said positively, "It's you and yours, madam, or me and mine. There isn't room for both of us."

Still carrying her coffee cup, she made her way to the broom closet, and with the help of a stout mop promptly disposed of mama tarantula and her young.

From that day on she began to feel less "green" in this new kind of life. She was now able to deal confidently with the wild-life which always competed with the New Englanders for possession of the ranch. By the time the rest of the rocket team arrived she was an expert at routing army ants from clothes closets, and hardly jumped when a coyote's howl drifted across the prairie in the dead of night.

Meanwhile Dr. Goddard, sporting a broad-brimmed West-

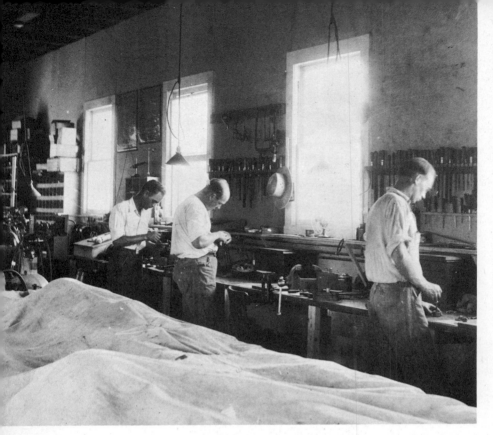

Shop interior along north side, with rocket covered,
to avoid dust and dirt

ern style hat, supervised the building of the thirty-by-sixty-foot workshop near the ranch house. By autumn the shop was ready to operate, and in December there was a good flight as a thrilling climax to the year.

The purpose of this test was to launch a rocket using an outside pressure-storage tank of compressed nitrogen gas. Dr. Goddard wanted to see whether, when this gas was released, its escape through tubes to the fuel and oxidizer tanks inside the rocket would have enough pressure to force the liquid oxygen and gasoline out of their tanks and into the combustion chamber.

The rocket itself carried a six-foot parachute, the handiwork of Mrs. Goddard, who thereby became official seamstress as well as photographer for the group. The parachute was bundled into an aluminum nose cone at the top of the

Early parachute, spring 1927 (Mr. Sachs is holding cone at greatest distance from rocket)

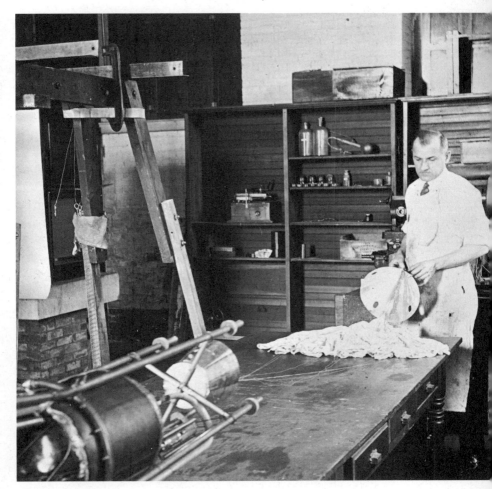

rocket. The plan was that the wind, coming from below as the rocket began to descend, would tear off the cone-shaped lid which extended over the rim of the rocket. Hopefully, the parachute would pop out and the rocket would slow down enough to land undamaged.

When the pressure gauge on the gas-generating chamber *outside* the rocket showed that two hundred pounds per square inch had built up in the storage tanks *inside* the rocket, the hose connecting the pressure cylinder and rocket was disconnected by pulling a cord. Then the igniter was fired, and the rocket allowed to rise two inches. For a moment it was held back, in order to build up more thrust. Then Dr. Goddard pulled a rope that released the pins which held the rocket between the vertical guides in the tower.

Nell rose quickly within the sixty-foot tower, building up

Flight tower and one shelter, 1930–1932 (Tower now on grounds of Roswell Museum)

a speed of between sixty and eighty miles an hour at the top. Upon reaching a height of two thousand feet above the tower, she was traveling at five hundred mph, and gradually became horizontal. The white flame disappeared, and, trailing a stream of grayish smoke, off Nell went, with a whistling sound which could be heard half a mile away, to land one thousand feet from the tower.

It was a very satisfactory flight. Dr. Goddard learned that it was possible to get a straight downward thrust from the chamber, so that the rocket's take-off would be straight upward for some time after launching.

By painting a broad red stripe down one side of the silvery rocket, he had been able to observe that it hardly twisted at all in its upward flight.

Everyone was pleased, though Mrs. Goddard was a little disappointed that her contribution, the parachute, had failed, and Nell's front end was fairly well bashed in.

"Never mind," her husband told her. "The time will come when we get her up and back in one piece with no trouble at all."

Next came a series of tests in order to develop a cooling system for the combustion chamber. Such high temperatures were built up when the rocket fuel was ignited that the chamber often burned right through near the narrow opening between the chamber and the nozzle.

None of the new metals Dr. Goddard tried seemed strong enough to overcome this difficulty. Redesigning the nozzle itself failed also. He found that by enlarging the throat of the nozzle he could avoid its burning through, but in the process he lost the concentrated thrust needed to lift the rocket.

Finally he hit upon a system which he thought would work, though at first it made no sense to his wife, who was trying valiantly to understand what was going on.

"How can you hope to cool the walls of the chamber with the same gasoline which makes such a fearful blaze when the oxygen is added?" she wanted to know.

"Oh, it'll burn, all right," explained her husband. "But even so, the protective layer of burning gas next to the inside wall of the chamber will be a whole lot cooler than the burning mixture of fuel and oxygen in the middle. You'll see."

Before long, he proved his point. The spraying of gasoline around the inner wall of the combustion chamber before it was ignited, or "curtain cooling" as he called it, solved the problem. No more rocket motors disintegrated from their own heat.

While all this was going on, Colonel Lindbergh watched Nell's progress like a fond godfather. He read Dr. Goddard's reports with interest and was very much pleased with Nell each of the three or four times he flew down to New Mexico to see what she was doing.

One day, shortly after the latest visit from Colonel Lindbergh, a neighbor stopped Dr. Goddard on the main street of Roswell.

"Oh, Dr. Goddard," she said kindly, "I've wanted to tell

you how badly I feel about all the trouble you've been having."

"Trouble?" asked Dr. Goddard, surprised.

"Why, yes—you poor soul! They say you've tried one gadget after another; but we haven't heard a flight in weeks. It must be *most* disheartening to fail again and again."

Dr. Goddard laughed. "But I'm not in the least disheartened," he protested. "After all, when a writer does an article or a book, he probably does a lot of rewriting, don't you suppose?"

"Why, I should think so," agreed the woman.

"And surely he doesn't consider his first draft a failure, or even his third or fourth."

"I quite understand, Dr. Goddard," she replied vaguely, giving his arm a consoling pat as she hurried off.

Dr. Goddard sighed. It was obvious she hadn't understood a word.

The next two years at Roswell were spent in achieving more flights, keeping the pressure constant, avoiding explosion of the combustion chambers by means of different cooling systems, studying strong, light materials, and making gyroscopes and other apparatus for guiding the rocket's flight.

As time went on, the rocket team dwindled temporarily. The lonely life was not to everyone's taste, and after a while two of Dr. Goddard's assistants went back East.

"I feel as if I'd lost my right arm," he mourned after seeing Henry Sachs off for home. "I wonder if anyone will ever

Rocket and crew, April 19, 1932 (Casing painted red on one side, to observe any rotation)

realize what a good machinist can mean to a project like this."

But Henry Sachs was replaced by "Oley" Ljungquist, a Worcester boy then living in California, and, with this one man for two, the work went on. It was particularly urgent now to get as much as possible accomplished before the first two-year period under the Guggenheim financing was up. Daniel Guggenheim had died during the first year of the Goddards' work in New Mexico, and the affairs of the Foundation were in some confusion. In addition, the great financial depression of the thirties was under way. It looked as if more money for the work in Roswell might not be forthcoming, after all.

One day in April 1932 the rocket group arrived at Eden Valley before daybreak, as they usually did on flight days, in hopes of getting the rocket up while there was no wind to throw her off course. The newest version of Nell rode behind the truck on a trailer.

For this flight, the rocket was equipped with something new. She carried an elaborate gyroscope to control the rocket's

Rocket being transported to launching tower,
fifteen miles northwest of Roswell, 1930–1932

Lower part of rocket, April 19, 1932, showing blast vanes

Gyroscope and mounting, tested May 20, 1932

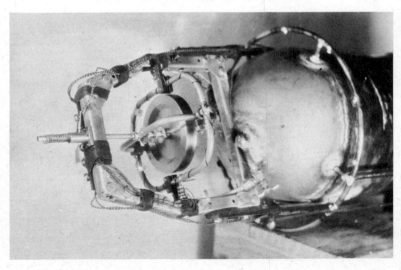

guiding vanes. These vanes, like rudders, were to keep the rocket flying straight by turning in the stream of gas from the nozzle, just as a boat's rudder works against the stream of the boat's wake. Besides this, the gyro was to release a parachute just before the rocket's ascent reached its peak.

When everything was ready, a key was pressed in the remote-control panel, a safe distance from the tower. It caused a pair of brass weights, attached to fishlines wound round and round the spindle of the gyro, to start to unwind. This started the gyro spinning. One of the five-pound weights, when it dropped, closed a switch, firing the igniter. The heat from this ignition melted a wire, allowing a third weight to drop and close another switch, freeing yet a fourth weight and turning on the gasoline. Nell had become more complex during the past months.

As far as the distance flown and the height reached were

Rocket controls being operated by R. H. Goddard — to fire, release, or stop test if firing unsatisfactory

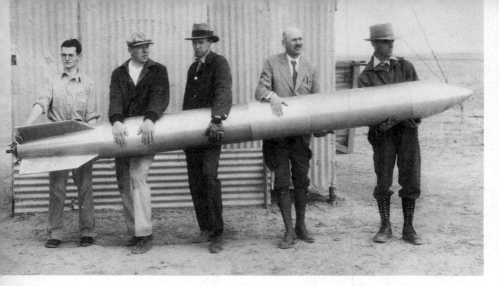

Rocket used in flight of April 19, 1932 (*Left to right:* L. Mansur, A. Kisk, C. Mansur, R. H. Goddard, N. Ljungquist)

concerned, this flight was not spectacular, but what Dr. Goddard really wanted to know was whether the vanes had worked.

It had seemed so, because the ascent had been perfectly vertical for a longer time than ever before. To make absolutely sure, the inventor and his men dashed off towards the point where the parachute had dropped out of sight, racing to see if any of the rocket vanes were still warm. If they were, it would certainly show that they had caught the stream of hot gas and done their job.

"Wait a minute!" he called back to Mrs. Goddard, who was running after them toward the truck. "Aren't you forgetting something?"

In her eagerness to be on hand to see how the vanes had worked, she *had* forgotten something. Among other things, one of her tasks was to stay behind after a flight and put out the grass fire that inevitably started at the base of the launching tower when a rocket took off.

"Darn," she muttered. Grabbing her trusty broom, she thumped away at the little tongues of flame, finishing off the job by dousing the area with a bucket of water.

That night Dr. Goddard wrote Colonel Lindbergh about the good flight. It seemed certain that the vanes had worked, since two of them had been found to be warmer than the others.

In May 1932 a meeting of scientists recommended that the Guggenheim grant be extended for another two years. But Daniel Guggenheim's estate was not settled. The Guggenheim Foundation decided there would be no more money to continue the work at Roswell, at least for the time being.

This news was a severe shock to the Goddards, and it was a sad day indeed when Dr. Goddard closed up the shop.

Rocket after flight, April 19, 1932

The morning of the day they left for home he went for one last look around.

The sober face of George Washington looked down on the empty laboratory from a calendar on the wall.

"Keep an eye on things," said Dr. Goddard. He went out the door, locking it behind him.

In a moment he popped in again. He put his broad-brimmed straw hat on one of the laboratory benches.

"I'll be back for this!" he promised.

Eight

Dr. and Mrs. Goddard went back home to Worcester, where he resumed teaching at the University. At the same time the Smithsonian Institution agreed once more to support his laboratory work on all sorts of rocket problems.

It felt good to be home again. "And wonderful to unlearn the habit of putting our shoes on a chair at bedtime to outwit the centipedes," Mrs. Goddard told a friend.

The most startling development to come forth from the next two years' work was a rocket chamber using atmospheric air as its oxidizer. This would seem to contradict the very definition of a rocket: actually, of course, a true rocket is unique because it carries its own oxidizer, and doesn't need air from outside. This latest invention was really an early form of the jet engine, which can never operate up where the air is thin. But for relatively low, horizontal flights, Dr. Goddard realized that such a motor could work very efficiently, since it would not be weighed down with liquid oxygen and its containers.

In the motor he devised at this time a funnel-shaped "mouth" gulped in air. The air passed through a shutter-type valve into the combustion chamber. As this shutter flapped open and shut at great speed, each release of air into the chamber came in a powerful spurt. The faster the air came in, the faster combustion could take place, and the greater was the resultant thrust. This process would be constant during flight.

A side effect of the system was the eerie noise produced by the resonance of the shutter valve. (This was the same noise that had a nerve-wracking effect when the Germans' "buzz-bomb," or V-I, flew over England a few years later in World War II. Dr. Goddard was astounded at this time when his patent lawyer told him that the Germans had hit upon his method.)

With the Guggenheim family's assurance that the New Mexico work could surely be resumed before long, it was perhaps a good thing to be able to take time to think about what he wanted to work on when he got back to Roswell. So the two years passed quickly.

By the fall of 1934, when it was possible to return to New Mexico, Dr. Goddard had a clear picture in his mind of what he needed to do next. The number of problems involved in the nitrogen-pressure systems he had tried during the original New Mexico adventure added up to one thing: too complicated to be dependable. A simple, fuel-feed system, even though it might weigh more, would be the best for good flight control and parachute release.

On this second trip to the Southwest, the Goddards stopped in Chicago for a look at the World's Fair.

"Well, this looks like something we should see!" said Dr. Goddard, reading the program of the day's events. "There'll be a 'space show' starting in ten minutes. Let's go!"

The show featured one Buck Rogers as the hero, complete with space helmet and "disintegrator ray gun." Another character was a Doctor Huer, whom the Goddards immediately recognized as a caricature of none other than Dr. Goddard himself.

Doctor Huer was the rocket scientist in charge of space flight who dealt with any problem that arose, very simply, by saying: "Now don't you worry. The old doctor will take care of everything!"

The Goddards left the show in fine spirits, and for some time thereafter Doctor Huer's line was a byword with them and the rocket crew.

Within hours of their return to the ranch, Dr. Goddard came hurrying into the kitchen where his wife was unpacking pots and pans.

"Company!" he announced cheerfully.

"*Company!*" she gasped. "And us without a stick of furniture in the house, and a can of hash for supper?"

"Oh, Colonel Lindbergh will understand," said her husband.

Mrs. Goddard sank weakly onto the kitchen stepladder, the one seat in the house.

"Don't say it!" she cried as her husband started to speak.

R. H. Goddard dusting off hat laid on shop bench, in June 1932, with hope of resuming work someday

"I know! 'The old doctor will take care of everything!'" And so he did. They all went to a hotel.

In a short while the shop was operating as if there had been no interruption. The old calendar picture of George Washington was exchanged for a 1934 version, and once more the first president looked down on a busy laboratory, where Dr. Goddard presided in his beloved hat.

The crew built a taller and stronger tower at the rocket range, and dug out a good-sized pit for observers at close range during static tests. They laid out an electric cable from the tower to another shelter, a thousand feet off, for the remote control of Nell's releasing devices before take-off.

At the new launching tower on March 8, 1935 there was more than the usual air of tense expectation. One member of the crew could be heard muttering to himself as he went about his tasks, complaining that Nell had been more fun in the early days, before she got so complicated.

"She was easier on the nerves, too," he added, observing the anxious faces around him. "But," he said to himself, "if she does her job today, I'll forgive her for getting so high and mighty."

"High and mighty" were just the words to describe Nell's performance that day.

A rocket launching today is preceded by the familiar and dramatic "count-down," but the launching of the Goddard rocket took place without fanfare.

Dr. Goddard pressed a button at the control station, and instantly there was a burst of flame and smoke at the base of the tower. A long, rumbling roar broke the desert quiet, and the splendid machine was up and away. Her characteristic high-frequency whine followed her as she went streaking across the vast New Mexico wasteland, at a speed undreamed-of before this day.

But Nell seemed determined to outdo herself in that spring of 1935. Not content with this first record-breaking supersonic flight, she strove for greater distance as well as high speed, and on May 31 the eighty-five-pound rocket flew seventy-five hundred feet—nearly a mile and a half.

During the summer there were other good flights, though it so happened that when Colonel Lindbergh and Mr. Harry

Charles A. Lindbergh and launching tower, September 23, 1935

Guggenheim arrived in September they saw what amounted to a good static test, not an actual flight. But the tremendous power of the rocket motor so impressed these two men that continued support from the Daniel and Florence Guggenheim Foundation became assured. That Mr. Harry Guggenheim should have so much faith in a device which he had never actually seen "used" was a tribute to his unusual perception in scientific matters.

The world was eager now for news of what was happening at Roswell, but Dr. Goddard kept still until he was ready to give a complete report on his progress. When this time came he prepared a paper for the Association for the

Advancement of Science, which he presented along with films on the last day of the year 1935, at St. Louis.

The press was ready for him. The entire front row of the hall was occupied by reporters hungry for any word about Nell. And they were not disappointed by what they heard and saw. While the scientists buzzed with excitement, crowding around the inventor with questions and congratulations, the newsmen raced back to their desks to spread the report of Nell's latest triumphs.

The new year opened with a big newspaper splash on GODDARD'S GREATEST ROCKET.

"And I suppose the next big news will make her 'Goddard's *greatest,* greatest rocket'!" said the inventor. It amused them that so much notice was taken of these spectacular, record-breaking flights, when they both felt that Nell's greatest steppingstone would not be passed until a dependable, self-contained pump system worked. And that would probably go unnoticed.

"Still," said Mrs. Goddard, "it certainly won't hurt if the government catches some of this enthusiasm, will it?"

Her husband agreed. Once more he was trying to get military people interested in the rocket, as they had begun to be just before the end of the First World War.

In 1937, Dr. Goddard went to Washington, fearing that the government's indifference to the rocket might be dangerous. While his own country ignored his ideas for rockets in warfare, Dr. Goddard was sure other countries were making

strides in rocketry. Potential enemies were probably bene-
fiting from his work, since his patents and publications were
available to anyone.

The German Army had had a rocket-testing station at an
artillery range near Berlin since 1932. Within two years
they had drafted for full-time military work every rocket
worker who hadn't fled the country.

But it seemed to be of no use to plead that *his* country
should be thinking along the same lines, that Dr. Goddard
and his people were willing and anxious to be drafted. "The
next war will be won with trench mortars," he was assured.

The inventor returned to Roswell deeply discouraged.

As usual after one of his trips, his wife met him at the
station. She had learned to expect him to look badly after
traveling alone, which he hated; but this time she was
shocked to see him so dejected.

"I wished I'd brought a wheelbarrow to pick up the pieces,"
she told him later.

But for the moment she very wisely said nothing, waiting
till her husband poured out his woes before telling him that
she, at least, had some good news.

Though their superiors seemed lukewarm about what Dr.
Goddard had to offer, the young officers of both the Army
Air Corps and Navy were very much excited about his experiments. For some time now a trip to Roswell had been a
sort of pilgrimage for these younger men, one of whom had
spent his precious leave hitchhiking from California to New
Mexico in order to see for himself what was going on.

"Now you've got a letter from a Lieutenant Boushey, at Langley Field," said Mrs. Goddard. "He says he's been studying rocket and jet-propulsion problems on his own. Now he feels he can't go further without help, and I gather he's about to beg, steal, or borrow an airplane to get down to see you! He sounds as if he half expects you to throw him out, poor thing, but he's coming anyway."

"What, me throw out the Air Corps?" asked Dr. Goddard. "Hardly!"

A long friendship began with the visit from this young officer. He was relieved to find that the famous scientist was nothing like the awesome and unapproachable person he'd expected to meet.

Lieutenant Boushey went away from his first visit determined to do all he could to get his superiors interested in the Goddard rocket.

Meanwhile, Nell continued to thrive, and there were so many fine flight tests in the winter and spring of 1938 that it seemed almost too good to be true. Then, in one violent hour, the picture changed.

On the evening of June 14 the rocket was secure in her tower and ready to go. But the wind showed no signs of dying down as it usually did in the late afternoon. If anything, it was more gusty than usual, so an attempt at flight was out of the question. Feeling decidedly uneasy about Nell under these conditions, Dr. Goddard arranged for one of the crew to stay through the night at the launching tower to keep an eye on her.

When he returned at five the next morning the rocket was steady enough, but she was being buffeted by ever stronger blasts of wind. After a final check of the guy wires and supports, he returned to the ranch, again leaving a man on guard at the tower.

During the day the wind continued to rise, with each successive blast outdoing the last, while the rocket team watched and listened anxiously.

At about four in the afternoon one of the men dashed into the Goddards' wing of the ranch house.

"It looks like a twister over Eden Valley!"

In minutes he was driving the Goddard crew toward the rocket range. The Ford truck, up to its hubcaps in drifted sand and debris, plunged gamely through what could be seen of the road—sometimes on it, sometimes off, but always stubbornly in the direction of Eden Valley.

"Pretty good traction on these tires, eh?" said the driver proudly.

"Amen," breathed Dr. Goddard.

"Nothing could happen to Nell, could it?" asked Mrs. Goddard. "Didn't you leave one of the men to watch her?"

Neither of them had seen a Southwestern "twister" before, but Dr. Goddard had been told about them. It was cold comfort to know that one of his men was guarding Nell now! The fact was that he was more concerned about his worker than about the rocket, but he didn't say so.

"Oh, she'll be fine, just fine."

When they were a mile or two short of the range, the wind

died down; the clouds of dust settled, and for the first time
that day the sun shone.

"There, now," said Mrs. Goddard happily. "It's all over."

It was all over, indeed. When the truck came to a stop
a few minutes later there was nothing to be seen of Nell and
the tower but a twisted wreck of metal tubing and electrical
wires.

Dr. Goddard jumped out of the truck.

"Charles!" he cried. There was no answer.

One of the men raced to Nell's trailer, parked thirty feet
from the truck. He had spied a man's boot poking out from
underneath, and to everyone's huge relief the boot was
moving. Out crawled Charles, completely covered with red
desert dust. Nearby lay a small rattler, very dead.

"Hello, everyone," he said in a dazed voice, looking up
at the relieved faces of his friends. "Boy, things sure happened fast around here!"

A little over an hour before, it seemed, Charles had been
putting covers around the lower end of the rocket.

"Then there was this terrific roar and a cloud of dust—and

Tower, after storm of July 15, 1938, with rocket in it—a disastrous day

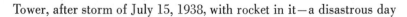

the next thing I knew I was waking up wrapped around one of those iron pipes that hold the guy wires."

He looked at the snake in a puzzled fashion.

"Oh, now I remember! I saw this rattler and chased it under the trailer and shot it. A good thing I did, too, from the looks of things," he added, seeing the heavy pieces of apparatus that had fallen all around. "Some of that stuff must have landed pretty hard!" He brushed the dust from his eyes and looked around. "Ooh," he moaned. "Nellie doesn't look so good."

This was such an understatement, and Charles looked so woebegone, that the Goddards had to laugh.

"She'll be up and around in no time," said Dr. Goddard, but seeing the wreck of months of labor scattered about him, he knew this just wasn't true. It would mean long, hard work before Nell and her tower and all her instruments could be rebuilt.

Bringing the first 20-foot section of the new tower
into place, July 1938

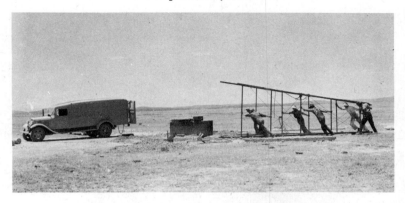

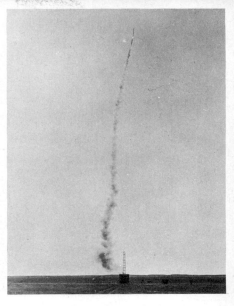

Setup for the flight
of August 9, 1938

The rocket in flight,
August 9, 1938

But she flew again in August; and she carried a new instrument. She was becoming so high-flying that the recording telescope had difficulty in tracking her. This time there
was a barograph aboard, a device which would record on a
roll of graph paper just what Nell had done in flight. A
committee from the National Aeronautic Association, who
had provided the instrument, was watching closely. If their
barograph could do its job, there would be dramatic evidence
to send to Washington.

Dr. Goddard hoped that this of all times would be one of
the flights when the parachute worked, so that they could
recover the barograph's findings.

For some moments after take-off it was impossible to tell
whether or not the parachute had opened. Nell had soared

The N.A.A. committee removing the barograph,
after flight of August 9, 1938

completely out of sight! But when she did reappear, a quarter
of a mile beyond the tower, the rocket people breathed sighs
of relief. She was descending in a ladylike fashion, supported
by her parachute.

The crew and the committee of observers gathered around
while the N.A.A. committee removed the barograph with
its paper record.

"Now, look at the line, boys," said Dr. Goddard. "Remember the 'pop' we heard just after she took off? Well, there
it is, where the line dips down at the beginning. Now," he
said, "here's where she went wobbly for a bit on the way
up. . . ."

By the time the entire picture of Nell's flight had been
studied, including the part when she had been completely
out of sight, the boys were jubilant.

The barograph was mailed to Washington, where the Goddards hoped it would be welcomed as proof of sound scientific work. At any rate, it was unquestionable evidence that the rocket was a mightily powerful machine.

"And now I want you to look at some research *I've* been doing," said Mrs. Goddard to her husband when they were home again. She produced a bulging envelope of printed material, and put it all out on his desk.

He saw pictures of a veritable paradise spread before him: *Hawaii, Land of Enchantment ... Moonlit nights and sundrenched days. ...*

She waited anxiously for her husband's reaction. Perhaps her suggestion of a vacation hadn't been subtle enough?

Dr. Goddard began to laugh.

"Now, let me show *you* something," he said. From his own file he pulled out a handful of folders.

Islands of Adventure and Romance ... read Mrs. Goddard. *Hawaii, Land of Enchantment ...*

She was speechless.

Dr. Goddard picked up the phone and dialed the travel agent. His wife couldn't bear to listen, so she retired to the kitchen to fumble with supper preparations while waiting to hear the outcome of the call.

A few minutes later her husband joined her.

"No Hawaii," he said.

She could hardly stand it, but was trying to think of a brave remark when Dr. Goddard added, "But there's space for us on the *Normandie*, sailing for Europe in ten days. We ought to see Europe, anyway, before it blows up in a Second World War."

Mrs. Goddard hardly heard the gloomy last part of this remark. In her mind's eye visions of sun-baked beaches and exotic tropical foliage were giving way to pictures of Paris, the cathedral at Chartres, and other sights she'd never dreamed of seeing. She was roused from her dream by the unmistakable smell of a forgotten something in the oven.

"Good heavens, the casserole!" she rushed to its rescue, meanwhile thinking furiously about how far she could stretch her secret savings from the household budget, so as to bring home something nice from Europe. A new set of china, perhaps, or a new rug. . . .

"That's it, a rug!" she said aloud.

When her husband asked what on earth she was muttering about, she explained dreamily that he would find out in due time, but right now supper was ready.

Nine

"Well, that was something!"

They had just returned from a day of sight-seeing. The cathedral at Chartres with the late afternoon sunlight pouring through the magnificent stained glass windows had been breathtaking, a sight always to be remembered, and a fitting climax to the trip. It had been all too short.

"But I'm sure we could wander about Europe for months, or even years, and still feel we'd just scratch the surface," said Mrs. Goddard.

"I suppose so," sighed her husband.

For the hundredth time she saw him secretly peeking at a travel folder describing the sights of Switzerland.

"I think I left my gloves at the desk," she said suddenly, and darted off. On the way down in the elevator she took a hurried look at her purse. Yes, the "rug fund" would cover this situation nicely.

She returned a short while later with a bundle of travel reservations in her handbag.

"Plans have changed," she announced. "We aren't going shopping tomorrow, we're going home."

Dr. Goddard's face fell.

"By way of Switzerland and London," she added.

Any disappointment at giving up the idea of an elegant carpet disappeared instantly. Her learned and dignified husband looked exactly like a child on Christmas morning.

He was still wearing this happy, dazed expression when their bus headed back to Paris. In London, on their way home, she had trouble getting him to leave the Victoria and Albert Museum before they were locked in at closing time. He had discovered the exhibit of apparatus used by Michael Faraday, whose experiments a century before had marked the beginning of the age of electricity.

"He actually had those things in his hands," marveled Dr. Goddard. It was impossible to tear him away until a guard politely told him that the museum was about to close. Before falling asleep that night, Mrs. Goddard reflected that perhaps one day people would look at her husband's inventions with the same awe he had felt on seeing the Faraday exhibit.

Back at Roswell again, Dr. Goddard started a new series of tests. Its purpose was to put into practice the theories about turbine-driven pumps which had been lying at the back of his mind since the time at Clark between the two New Mexico adventures.

For long-range flights it was necessary to lighten the

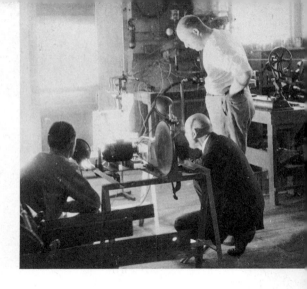

Conducting a pump test in Roswell shop, fall 1938

rocket's load as much as possible, so he went to work to devise a lightweight pump-turbine unit that might give tremendous thrust with a fuel-feeding system that would be self-sustaining.

Whereas in former Goddard rockets liquid gasoline and oxygen had been forced into the chamber by the escaping of nitrogen from a tank *within* the rocket, the inventor was convinced that it would be possible to do without this tank, and thereby reduce the weight of the rocket.

He would design a centrifugal pump system which would be self-sustaining once it got going. There would be one pump between the oxygen tank and the combustion chamber, and another one between the gasoline tank and the chamber.

But how to start the pumps pumping? And once started, what would keep them going?

The answer to both problems lay in the creation of a turbine drive. The turbine wheels, like the blades of rotary fans,

Completed rocket for first test with pumps and turbines. January 6, 1939

were to be mounted on a shaft inside the rocket, one for each of the two pumps. The wheels were to be set spinning by a high-speed flow of nitrogen through a tube from a tank outside the rocket. The wheels would turn, the shaft would turn, the pumps would pump. Now the line from the outside tank would be disconnected, and the rocket would be in operation.

But now for the second problem—keeping her that way.

Dr. Goddard piped a connection from the chamber jacket to the turbines. While most of the hot gases produced by combustion would rush out the nozzle as before, some of the heat would vaporize through this connection. This vapor, under pressure, would turn the wheels and keep the pumping process going.

It might seem that with a satisfactory pump design, this phase of the work could be considered complete. But there was still the crucial question of the *weight* of the new

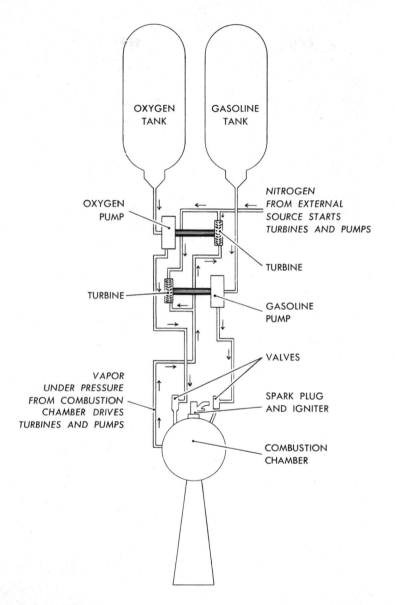

OXYGEN
TANK

GASOLINE
TANK

OXYGEN
PUMP

NITROGEN
FROM EXTERNAL
SOURCE STARTS
TURBINES AND PUMPS

TURBINE

TURBINE

GASOLINE
PUMP

VALVES

VAPOR
UNDER PRESSURE
FROM COMBUSTION
CHAMBER DRIVES
TURBINES AND PUMPS

SPARK PLUG
AND IGNITER

COMBUSTION
CHAMBER

Simplified diagram of fueling system showing pumps and turbines pumps. It didn't matter how bulky they might be in a static test; but for Nell to fly with them, as they were, would defeat one purpose of their design.

Pump manufacturers all over the country merely shook their heads when confronted with the problem. What, build a pump from metal that was lightweight and yet able to stand up under the low temperatures of liquid oxygen and the high speeds required?

"Poor old Nellie. She's got the worst growing pains we've ever seen!" said the Goddards, as each improvement merely made the rocket more complicated and less movable.

This was the usual pattern in the development of new devices, however, and they were well used to it by now. First there would be a period when things were more difficult and complex than ever before. Then suddenly all would take a turn for the better.

And so Dr. Goddard and his crew again bravely turned to fashioning another pioneer device for Nell.

The turning point came in 1940, when the new pumps had been consolidated to the point where a man could hold

Pump-turbine rocket, February 6, 1940: overall length, 22 feet, diameter 18 inches; weight, loaded, about 500 pounds (now in National Air Museum, Washington, D. C.)

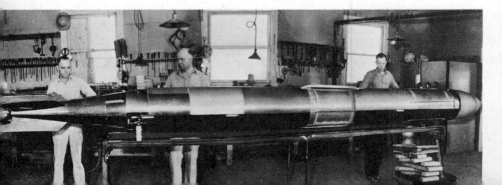

Closeup of Mr. Ljungquist holding pumps, April 1940 (liquid oxygen pump at left; gasoline pump at right)

one in each hand. One was for oxygen and one for gasoline, and each contained in miniature the mechanism used in the early static tests of the turbine driven pump.

These handfuls of apparatus were to drive a rocket which, loaded, weighed close to five hundred pounds!

In the summer of 1940 and the spring of 1941, Nell flew successfully fueled by these two pumps.

"*Now* they can talk about Goddard's greatest rocket!" said one of the men proudly. Whatever might be said about the long, high flights back in the mid-thirties, this was Nell's great day as far as the Goddards were concerned. "The day the pumps worked" was one they long remembered.

Rocket leaving tower, using pumps for propellants, August 9, 1940

At last important military people were beginning to think about how to use the rocket.

Lieutenant Boushey had been stationed at Wright Field, and all this while he had been urging anyone who would listen to support Dr. Goddard. He seemed to be making progress, and by 1940 he had even found a government agency which might have funds to spend on the work. But the drawing up of a contract dragged on and on. Finally Dr. Goddard himself went to see if things could be speeded up. After sitting out an entire day in an office waiting room, he concluded that the Army was not interested in him and his rocket.

So he listened to the proposition of the Navy, which was also sending an emissary to Roswell, and in September 1941 he was asked to start preliminary work right away. A little later the Air Corps also made a contract with him.

Working for the government made a change in the Goddards' way of life in Roswell. They could talk even less about what they were doing, and the operation at Mescalero Ranch was under armed guard twenty-four hours a day.

Once again they had occasion to be grateful to the open minds of the people who lived in open spaces. When the inventor explained that he was working on government business now, something he couldn't tell them about, his friends let him alone and asked no questions.

Thus Dr. Goddard and his men were already hard at work for the government when the Japanese attacked Pearl Harbor on December 7. Later, as the war worsened in both

Preliminary pressure-tank thrust unit, for Navy JATO, December 1941 (spherical tanks for lox and gasoline; helium cylinder at left)

Europe and the Orient, the Navy asked Dr. Goddard to come East and work with their people at Annapolis, Maryland.

"I guess we'll have to close up shop for the duration," said Dr. Goddard. "Nell's been drafted."

But he hoped to return, one day, and carry on the work which had gone so well at Roswell. Right now the winning of the war was the most important thing.

From the wartime work that Dr. Goddard did with the Army and Navy came, among other things, the development of JATO, the jet-assisted take-off using solid propellants.

Setup for final test of JATO unit at Roswell, June 27, 1942, before leaving for Annapolis

An early test of JATO unit, showing excess of smoke

Test of Navy JATO unit at Roswell, New Mexico, showing somewhat
improved combustion

Further improvement of combustion, at Roswell, New Mexico, in
variable thrust pump unit

Test of JATO unit, showing pointed, striated flame, and steady, larger
flame, with variable thrust pump-turbine unit; at Roswell, New Mexico

Test of jet-assisted take-off unit, using liquid propellants, on a PBY;
Severn River, Maryland, September 23, 1942

Next came the assignment of developing a rocket motor
with variable thrust controllable by a pilot.

"What does *that* mean? Why 'variable thrust'?" asked
Mrs. Goddard.

"It means quite a problem," explained her husband.
"They want a rocket motor on an airplane, as dependable as
a water faucet, so that a pilot can speed it up or slow it down
just the way you turn water from a tap off and on, with no
leaks, lags, or spurts. The slightest miscalculation would mean
a leak of gas or liquid oxygen—and then *Boom!*"

Mrs. Goddard could understand why her husband looked
so worried nowadays. This was quite an assignment! He
would leave for the Experimental Station so early in the
morning that he drove to work with the car headlights turned
on. They were on again by the time he reached home.

This schedule meant long, lonely hours for her, since she
could no longer help with the rocket work, which was now
mostly "top secret."

It occurred to Mrs. Goddard that, with Johns Hopkins
University only a few miles away, this was her chance to

finish college. She might be a bit rusty in some subjects, after years away from school, but no one could say she hadn't kept up the habit of studying. And someone who had learned as much as she had about a subject like rocketry shouldn't have too much trouble getting back into the swing of college work, her husband insisted. Hoping the University would feel the same way, she applied for admission and was accepted.

On her way home from her interview Mrs. Goddard decided that this was a good excuse for a celebration. She counted up her treasured "red points"—the tokens that were allotted for scarce foods during the war—and found that there were enough for a really fine roast of beef. She bought all the trimmings, too, not forgetting the traditional celebration cigar for her husband.

That night, as time went by and her husband didn't turn up, she grew more and more uneasy about this piece of pure gold that was wasting away in the oven.

When the phone rang she knew what to expect.

"I guess I'll be a little late," said Dr. Goddard sheepishly.

"You already *are!*" wailed his wife.

It seemed that the car had refused to start, for the very good reason that there was no gas in the tank. And what was worse, there was no money in the pocket. It never failed to amaze Mrs. Goddard that this methodical man, who could keep track to the last penny of how much Nell was costing, never knew or cared whether he had a cent in his wallet or in the bank.

"Take a taxi, and hurry!" she said. "I'll pay the driver when you get here." She hung up and raced to the kitchen to turn off the oven.

"Taxis, yet," she said to herself as she checked her own pocketbook. "It had better be a pretty good meal!" When Dr. Goddard finally arrived, Mrs. Goddard paid the driver and waited impatiently for him to leave. But he stood there, looking huge and hungry, sniffing the good smells from the kitchen.

"Mmm, roast beef, I'll bet," he said wistfully. "And potatoes? And pie?"

"That's right," said Mrs. Goddard. Hating herself, she eased him out the door.

"Poor soul. He *did* look hungry," she said.

"Ha!" snorted Dr. Goddard. "You can be sure he and his family will eat very nicely tonight, on what that taxi ride cost."

With both the Goddards working hard, the years at Annapolis passed quickly. To the amazement of the military, the newly created, horizontal Nell was able to do what the Navy and Army Air Corps had asked of her. The specifications they wanted were practically impossible, but she had done the impossible before—and did it again this time.

The rocket plane motor was able to perform as dependably as the water faucet Dr. Goddard had used as an illustration to explain variable thrust. It could idle for fifteen seconds, which would be necessary before take-off, and then race up to the three-hundred-pound pressure needed for the twenty

seconds during which the plane would become airborne.
Then five seconds of idling while it would level off, immediately followed by five hundred pounds of thrust for flight.
This remarkable range of speed in the new motor meant that
a pilot in combat could make either a quick pursuit or a lightning getaway.

When the research plane called the X-2, (for "experimental supersonic,") passed the speed of sound a few years
later, it used this kind of motor. The X-15 uses it now.

Dr. Goddard's final project at Annapolis was a small pres-
sure-fed liquid-oxygen gasoline rocket, possibly adaptable to
a small guided missile.

His exhausting work schedule began to affect his health,
and brought back symptoms that seemed at first to point to
his old lung trouble. For a time, he stubbornly kept on working despite a constant cough. Then after a while it became
painful even to speak, and as much as possible he wrote out
what he wanted to say.

By the time his doctors persuaded him that he must go to
the hospital, he seemed almost indifferent—too tired to care.

But he did have the thrill, just before entering the hospital, of seeing Mrs. Goddard get her degree, with honors,
from Johns Hopkins. No accomplishment of his own had
pleased him more. For that day, at least, he looked almost
like his old self.

When the doctors operated, they found that cancer had
attacked a larynx already weakened by the long-ago battle

with tuberculosis. They hoped he could be made strong enough to withstand a second operation, but despite blood transfusions he grew more feeble.

Late one stifling night in August, when Mrs. Goddard had barely reached home from the day at her husband's bedside, a call came from the hospital. The night nurse said that Dr. Goddard seemed very restless and disturbed. He wanted his wife to come back at once, as there was something he must tell her.

Hurrying back to the hospital, she found him too weak to speak. He recognized her, smiled, and fell back on the pillow, exhausted.

"I thought this might happen," whispered the nurse. "A little while after I called you I could see he was already too tired to talk. But he showed me he wanted his writing pad when I asked what he needed to see you about."

Mrs. Goddard took the note pad and read the words: *About a thousand things!*

These four words spoke volumes, she reflected on the lonely train ride home. The thousand shared experiences, the plans for a thousand things still undone. . . .

Within a few days it was over. There simply was not enough strength for another battle.

A few years later, a permanent memorial exhibit of Dr. Goddard's rocket apparatus was opened in New York, and Mrs. Goddard was there as a speaker and guest of honor. It was a wonderful thing to see her husband's acomplishments recognized in this way.

The opening of the Goddard Rocket Exhibit, at the American Museum of Natural History in New York, April 21, 1948 *(Left to right:* Mrs. Goddard, Harry F. Guggenheim, J. H. Doolittle. Rocket now in the National Air Museum at Washington)

But next morning reaction set in after the excitement of the opening. Oh, to be alone for a bit! But not alone in a hotel room. Thinking over all the places in New York where she might be reasonably certain of peace and quiet, it occurred to her that if she were to go back to the Memorial Exhibit for a quiet visit with Nell, she would surely have the place to herself. Since it had just opened, there certainly wouldn't be any visitors yet, she thought.

She was mistaken!

No sooner had she settled herself on a bench in a dark corner of the hall than the double doors burst open, and what seemed like at least a hundred schoolchildren streamed in, shepherded by an earnest young schoolteacher.

Well, they certainly had a right to be here, she thought, and they seemed interested, which was good. She waited patiently, and in due time the class filed out in orderly fashion, leaving her alone.

It was a few minutes before she realized that she was not *quite* alone, after all. A few yards away a small boy stood with his back to her, peering up intently at the great twenty-two-foot Nell.

"You're apt to get left behind," said Mrs. Goddard.

But the boy paid no attention, and continued to stare at the gleaming, streamlined beauty. A moment later he turned to her, solemn-eyed.

"Let me tell you something, lady," he said.

Mrs. Goddard smiled. "I wish you would!"

"You see that pump?" the boy pointed. "And that gyroscope? He actually had those things in his hands! And if he were alive today, there'd be a whole lot of other things he'd be working on, even better."

"That's right," agreed Mrs. Goddard. "A thousand things, most likely. But now you and your friends will have to take care of that for him, won't you?"

Bibliography

GODDARD, ROBERT H. *A Method of Reaching Extreme Altitudes.* Smithsonian Miscellaneous Collections, LXXI (1919), no. 2.
Rocket Development. New York, Prentice-Hall, 1948.

GOTTLIEB, WILLIAM P. *Jets and Rockets and How They Work.* New York, Garden City Books, 1959.

HENDRICKSON, WALTER B., JR. *Handbook for Space Travellers.* New York, Bobbs-Merrill, 1959.

LAWRENCE, MORTIMER W. *The Rockets' Red Glare.* New York, Coward-McCann, 1960.

TRUAX, ROBERT C. *Dawn of the Space Age.* 1956 edition Britannica *Book of the Year.*

The World Book Encyclopedia: Chicago, Field Enterprises, 1956.

Index